Our Debt to Greece and Rome

EDITORS
GEORGE DEPUE HADZSITS, PH.D.

DAVID MOORE ROBINSON, PH.D., LL.D.

ENGINEERING

BY

ALEXANDER PURVES GEST, C.E.

COOPER SQUARE PUBLISHERS, INC.

NEW YORK

1963

Published 1963 by Cooper Square Publishers, Inc.
59 Fourth Avenue, New York 3, N. Y.
Library of Congress Catalog Card No. 63-10287

INTRODUCTION

MODERN engineering has become so extended and specialized in all directions, that its relation to ancient engineering, if such a thing exists, is apparently almost inconceivable. The relation does exist, however, in a marked and interesting manner and Mr. Gest has laid engineers of the present time and others interested in the subject, under a debt of obligation to him for the interesting volume he has produced.

If one were to examine the plans of the Catskill Aqueduct recently completed as an extension of the public water supply of the City of New York, with its many detailed features required to collect and control the 600 m.g. of flow per day, it would be found that the water supply of ancient Rome, with its wonderful aqueducts constructed nearly 2,000 years ago, some of them still supplying the city, furnished a comparison of no mean character, but on the contrary one calculated to indicate that after all in their many features, and in their principal functions, the advances exhibited in the modern structure are certainly no more than ought to be expected in a period of two thousand years. In fact, the modern constructors would sacrifice no self-respect in giving to their ancient colleagues unqualified praise for what they did. One might go further and state that Frontinus as the Water Commissioner of Rome and one of the first possibly that we know much about in ancient times, discharged his duties with all the efficiency of the best of his modern colleagues and under circumstances no less perplexing or exasperating than those under which they frequently suffer at the present time.

The engineering productions or attainments of any given time are in reality an accurate and clear indication of some of the principal characteristics of the nations in which the results of engineering practice are found. The water works, roads and other engineering structures which were built so effectively in ancient Roman territory showed that the Romans were born engineers and builders. They were resolute in what they undertook, they were good thinkers, not only in the engineering field but in other professional fields. They understood the functions of good government and on the whole developed it. Indeed, the attainment of such creditable results in the engineering profession could not have been realized in a nation of different character. The Greeks were given to literature, the arts and to a considerable extent to mathematical science, but their attainments in the engineering profession were far short of those of the Romans.

The refinements of efficiency and excellence to which our bridge building in its various fields has been brought in consequence of the remarkable advances made in the production of iron, steel, cement and other required materials, has obviously no parallel in ancient engineering. It is true that the Romans had their volcanic Pozzolana, a material which enabled them to produce a hydraulic cement of such excellent character that sound specimens of concrete have been found nearly two thousand years old. In iron and steel, however, their products were of the crudest and they were able to make no material adaptation of them in the field of bridge construction. They did, however, attain remarkable excellence in masonry arches and other structures, using natural stone for their purpose. Indeed, it is probable that the great majority of their principal masonry works were accomplished without the use of cement joints, requiring an accuracy in dimensions of the stones to which we today do not attain.

Although Mr. Gest restricts his researches chiefly to the Greeks and Romans as the richest fields and undoubtedly the most striking in character, the remains of interesting and extensive engineering works are to be found in both Egypt and Assyria, and the general characteristics of those nations will be found to correspond with the engineering constructions in which they engaged in the centuries far more remote than those in which the Greek and Roman works belong. We hope that it may eventually be possible to secure reliable knowledge as to the buildings constructed by those ancient peoples which would undoubtedly show that both the art and science of building construction had taken effective shape in a prehistoric period and that the degree of civilization reached by them closely corresponded to such constructions.

It is both fascinating and highly profitable to develop from the results of investigations in ancient engineering works, the original plans adopted for the purpose of meeting the requirements of large buildings or an extensive system of canals fitted with control works necessary to provide for canal navigation, like those found in the Euphrates Valley, or again the design of great storage reservoirs like the Fayûm in the Upper Nile basin, or to take another illustration, the plans for quarrying and handling the blocks of stone required in the construction of pyramids. It is now largely a matter of speculation, how these ancient engineers planned and executed their works, but enough has already been disclosed to show that the modern engineer has not been the only engineer to meet and solve difficulties, or to make the best use of the means at his command to accomplish great engineering works.

WM. H. BURR

PREFACE

IN ORDER to appreciate our Debt to Greece and Rome, as illustrated by Engineering, it is necessary to show some connection between the old engineering and the new. At first sight it may be thought that there is no continuity between the engineering of the ancient and of the modern world and that no connection can be traced. This was my earlier opinion; but reading and reflection have taught me that the connection referred to is as real in the field of engineering as it is, for example, in that of literature or of law.

Engineering is so closely connected with material progress that the history of engineering parallels the history of civilization; and just as the Greek and Roman civilization, as a whole, profoundly affected the civilization of modern Europe, we discover that the ancient engineering, so important a factor in the old civilization, is an equally important factor in our Debt.

Further, as engineering achievements of the Romans were not confined to Rome. or even to

Italy, but were extended throughout all of their provinces, and were one of the means of promoting their civilization, a brief review of the characteristic features of the Roman dominion will help us to gain a clearer view of the relation of their engineering works to the people of the provinces and to the people who came after them. The intention of this book is, rather, to indicate the relation of Greek and Roman engineering to the Debt which modern civilization owes to Greece and Rome, than to present a technical account of ancient engineering, such as an engineer would naturally require.

At the same time it has seemed important to make that account sufficiently comprehensive to show the magnitude and extent of the ancient works, whose remains are found everywhere through the old empire, and which included every variety of engineering then possible.

It has been my aim to avoid unnecessary technicalities, but, owing to the nature of the subject, it has been impossible to avoid them altogether. Those who desire more complete information are referred to the exhaustive treatises of the French engineers Leger and Choisy, and to the valuable German works of Merckel and Durm, to the descriptions of the aqueducts by Mr. Clemens Herschel, to the works of the eminent Italian archaeologist Rodolfo Lanciani, and to Professor Burr's *Ancient and Modern Engineering;* to these and to many others I am indebted for details of information and to them all I freely acknowledge my obligations.

I also gratefully acknowledge the material assistance of the Editors of the series, who, besides their careful revision of my manuscript, have contributed some portion of the text, thereby notably enhancing the archaeological and literary value of the book.

CONTENTS

ENGINEERING

ENGINEERING

I. INTRODUCTORY

LORD BRYCE, in the preface to his *Studies in History and Jurisprudence*, has said: " The longer one lives, the more one is impressed by the close connection between the Greco-Roman world and our own."

This connection between the old world and the new, so readily traced in the history of modern civilization, has been less generally recognized in engineering than in other lines; the old engineering has often been considered as a department of archaeology rather than a real factor in the development of the modern world; and modern engineering practice is, at first sight, so dissimilar to the ancient as to seem an entirely new art, quite independent of the old.

This view is supported by the fact that with the downfall of the Roman empire, and the destruction of its efficient and highly centralized organization, engineering construction practically ceased, and was only gradually resumed as demanded by the necessities of a new or reviving civilization; nevertheless it is also true that the Roman tradition endured throughout the intervening period, and the new engineering was developed under the influence of Roman tradition, as well as guided by Roman example. To form a proper appreciation of the extent of that influence, and consequently a juster measure of our Debt to Greece and Rome, in that respect, requires, at least, some brief preliminary sketch of the growth of Rome and her provinces.

After driving out the Etruscan kings, the Romans, by a succession of conquests, acquired dominion over all Italy, south of the Rubicon; then followed the defeat of Carthage, to the south, that of Greece and of Mithridates, in the east, the acquisition of Spain, Gaul, and part of Britain, in the west, and the subsequent acquisition of other territories, until in the time of Trajan, the vast Roman empire was bounded on the north by the waters of the Rhine and the Danube, reached on the east to the Black and Caspian Seas, controlling Northern Africa looked to the Desert of the

Sahara, and was limited to the west only by the Atlantic Ocean.

This great domain had appeared in vision to the Roman poet who described it in these famous lines of intensest patriotism:

> *Horrenda late nomen in ultimas*
> *Extendat oras, qua medius liquor*
> *Secernit Europen ab Afro*
> *Qua tumidus rigat arva Nilus,*
>
> . . . . . .
>
> *Quicumque mundo terminus obstitit,*
> *Hunc tangat armis, visere gestiens,*
> *Qua parte debacchentur ignes,*
> *Qua nebulae pluviique rores.*

That control continued until A.D. 395, when the Empire was divided, never to be re-united again. Visigoths, Huns, and Vandals swept on to Rome. In A.D. 410, the City of the Seven Hills, so long inviolate from foreign enemies, was taken by Alaric; another Visigoth, Theodoric, saved Rome from Attila in A.D. 451, but, finally, in A.D. 476, another Romulus, by a strange freak of fortune, "Romulus Augustulus" abdicated as last emperor in Rome. Claudian, meantime, had, in the spirit of Horace, drawn an immortal picture of Rome at the zenith of her power, though even then on the eve of her decline:

" . . . (*we*) *watch the far-off foam*
Break upon Thule's shore and call it play,
Or through dim, dreadful forests force our way,
That we may tread Orontes', Ebro's shore —
That we are all one nation evermore! "

But even in and after the fifth century, because of " the fall of the Empire in the West," the Roman empire did not suddenly vanish; Constantinople had merely become its capital.

It was a distinguishing characteristic of the Romans that they carried their civilization with them to the countries that they conquered; though often unjust and oppressive in the administration of their provincial governments, they were wise enough to see that the permanence of their dominion depended upon the loyalty and contentment of their subjects, and consequently, after they had reduced a nation to subjection, they devoted their energies to the development of the country and to the promotion of the welfare of the people.

The result of this policy is thus summed up by Gibbon: " The same salutary maxims of

government, which had secured the peace and
obedience of Italy, were extended to the most
distant conquests. A nation of Romans was
gradually formed in the provinces," and further on he adds: " it was by such institutions
that the nations of the empire melted away into
the Roman name and people."

The rapidity with which the Gauls adopted
Roman customs is well known, and the ready
acceptance of Roman civilization by the na-
tives of Britain has been characterized by Professor Haverfield as " automatic."

At the time of the Roman conquest Britain
was covered with forests, there was no agriculture, except where some Belgian colonists
had settled on the shores of Kent; when the
Romans left Britain, the country was well settled, with many prosperous villages and cities
connected by a well-developed system of public
roads, and agriculture had so advanced that the
Emperor Julian was able to relieve a famine in
the Rhine valley by large shipments of grain
from Britain. At the same time education was
not neglected; in speaking of an inscription
presumably written by a workman, Professor
Haverfield remarks that in the countries ruled
by Rome the education of the people was fur-

ther advanced than at any time after the fall of the empire until the year 1848.

Of the benefits derived from the Roman occupation Camden writes, with reference to Ireland: " I cannot be persuaded that the island was conquered by the Romans. Without question, it had been well for it, if it had, as it would have been a means to civilize the nation. For, wherever the Romans were conquerors, they introduced humanity among the conquered, and except where they ruled, there was no such thing as humanity, learning or politeness in any part of Europe "; and Cobden, in similar words attributes the misfortunes of Ireland to the " circumstance of the Romans having never colonized it," and he declares that, " if they had occupied it for three centuries and a half, they would perhaps have left it more advanced than it proved to be in the sixteenth century."

Fortunately for the preservation of the civilization which Rome had diffused throughout the provinces, the decline of the Empire was gradual. Internal causes contributed to that decline as much as external; slavery, decay of trade and commerce, taxation, loss of moral fibre aided the barbarians from without. But

meantime those very barbarians were learning
Roman methods of warfare and, better still,
Roman lessons of civilization, so that Ataulf,
king of the West Goths, could declare it to be
his desire to go down to posterity as the restorer
and maintainer of the Roman power.

Even more astonishing was the career of
Theodoric, the Ostrogoth, who conquered Italy
in A.D. 493. His policy was conspicuously ben-
eficent and enlightened. As ruler of Italy, it
was his determination to preserve all that was
best in the government of his predecessors; he
revived agriculture in the peninsula, repaired
ancient roads and aqueducts, restored public
monuments in Rome, was a patron of letters,
honoring Boëthius, and, through him, continuing the influence of the classical spirit, all
but succeeding in uniting the Western world
again under a single ruler.

It was in great part due to the continued
influence of this Roman spirit, and to its persistence after the fall of the pagan Empire and
after the rise of Christianity, that the engineering works of the period preceding the Renaissance were so generally imitations of the works
of the Romans; and when, with the revival of
learning, engineering once more became a pro-

fession, the engineers of the period were largely guided by their veneration for all things Roman, as well as by their admiration of the Roman works which they accepted as their models and examples.

II. EARLY ENGINEERING WORKS

THE ancient Egyptians, who were so dependent upon the annual inundations of the Nile, were the pioneers in hydraulic engineering; their works for confining the flood waters of the river to their proper channel, and for controlling the distribution of the water by irrigating canals, were of such remote antiquity that their construction was attributed to Osiris. Prominent among these works was the great lake or reservoir known as Lake Moeris, said to have been constructed in the twenty-third century B.C., for the purpose of controlling and regulating the overflow of the Nile during the inundations. Some distance south of Memphis, and eight or ten miles west of the Nile, is a low-lying district, separated from the river by the Libyan hills, and now occupied in part by a lake, called Birket-el-Kerûm. A canal, connecting with the river, was cut through a gap in the hills; and the low lands of the Fayûm were surrounded by a great impounding dam. The lake thus formed received the flood waters of the Nile, and, as the inundation subsided, the water returned in part to the river through the same channel, thus equalizing the flow, and a part was used to supply a system of irrigating canals, the flow of the water through these canals being regulated by sluices and gates, under the control of the government. Maspero, who doubts the existence of any artificial work at Lake Moeris, excepting the enlargement of a natural channel, describes these canals as being from twenty to sixty or seventy feet wide, and extending from their source to the seaboard; they were generally straight in outline, but occasionally made wide detours to avoid irregularities in the topography. Dikes were built from the hills to the river, dividing the area into a series of artificial basins; these dikes were usually earthworks, although sometimes built of burnt bricks and sometimes of dressed stone. Of the latter class was the great dike built at the time of the founding of the city of Memphis, in order to divert the course of the river from the site selected for the city.

The canal connecting the Nile and the Red Sea is said to have been begun in the fourteenth

or fifteenth century B.C.; its completion, undertaken by Necho, about 610 B.C., was abandoned by him after 120,000 men had lost their
lives in the excavation; the work was afterwards resumed by Darius and, according to
Herodotus, was completed by him; but, according to Strabo, Darius left it unfinished on
the representation of his engineers that the
water of the Red Sea was higher than the Nile.
The canal was finally completed by Ptolemy II,
who, Strabo says, constructed locks with mov-
able gates so that boats could enter and leave
the canal whenever they pleased; thus antici-
pating by about seventeen centuries the invention of lock gates for canals, usually attributed
to Leonardo da Vinci. Pliny gives the dimensions of the canal as 100 feet wide, 40 feet deep,
and 37 miles long.

The entire region between the Euphrates and
the Tigris was covered by a network of canals,
intended primarily for irrigation but large
enough for navigation by small boats; the in-
takes at the rivers were protected by dams,
which Strabo calls " artificial cataracts," and
they are said to have been provided with sluices
and gates to regulate the flow of the water; the
dams in the Tigris were removed by Alexander

the Great, because they prevented his ships from descending the river.

In the reign of Darius, the Persian empire was provided with a system of highways, on which a courier or messenger service was established, similar to the *Cursus Publicus* of the Romans.

The Carthaginians, like the Persians, were road builders. Bergier refers to Isidorus as his authority for the statement that the Carthaginians were the first to build paved roads. Isidorus' words are: " Primi autem Poeni dicuntur lapidibus vias stravisse; postea Romani eas per omnem paene orbem disposuerunt " (xv. 16. 6). Leger goes further and says that from them the Romans " borrowed the idea "; this is possible, as the Romans had treaty relations with their Carthaginian rivals before the construction of the Appian Way, and they were never averse to learning from friend or foe; *fas est ab hoste doceri*. It is very doubtful, however, whether such was the case; the belief seems to rest on the unsupported dictum of Isidorus regarding the priority of the Carthaginians in road-building. Isidorus gives no authority; wrote about the year 600, nine centuries after the building of the Appian Way, and at best only mentions a tradition. Even if it be true, it can only be in the same sense as the Romans are said to have borrowed the arch from the Etruscans, or the Greeks to have learned geometry from the Egyptians.

Herodotus devotes several pages of his history to the people of Samos, and apologizes, twice in the same chapter, for doing so, because " three of the greatest works in all Greece " were constructed by them. One of these was a tunnel, eight feet in height and width and nearly a mile long, under a hill nine hundred feet high; within the tunnel was a channel three feet wide in which were laid pipes to conduct water into the city; the engineer was Eupalinus of Megara. The second was a breakwater protecting the harbor, and the third a temple of Hera, built by the architect Rhoecus of Samos, about 640 B.C. and notable for " being the largest known." Perhaps contemporaneous with the aqueduct of Samos was the aqueduct constructed by King Hezekiah to supply the city of Jerusalem.

A celebrated prehistoric work of the Greeks was the emissary or drainage tunnel of Lake Copais [1] in Boeotia. This lake receives the flow of the Cephissus and of several other small streams, but the natural outlet to the sea is obstructed by a range of limestone hills, and the water found its outlet through several subterranean passages. So long as these passages remained free of obstruction, the land was one of the most prosperous districts of Greece; but after they became choked, the district became a lake in rainy seasons and at other times a bog. Crates, an engineer in the service of Alexander the Great, undertook to re-open the obstructed channels and had made some progress in the work when compelled to abandon it on account of party strife among the Boeotians. The lake has now been drained by the construction of a tunnel through the hills; the lowering of the water level has disclosed, on the bed of the old lake, three lines of drainage canals, extending the entire length of the lake, with numerous branches, forming a complete drainage system; these canals are partly in excavation, and in part consist of a series of earthen dikes strengthened in places by walls of solid cyclopean masonry, which collected the water and led it to the entrances of the underground channels. Indications were also found of the existence of two partially completed tunnels, one in nearly the same location as the modern tunnel, which is about 2,200 feet long; the other, through the hill at the eastern end of the lake, would have been, if completed, over a mile and a quarter long; on the southeastern shore of the lake are the ruins of an old cutting about 90 feet deep. It is supposed that the drainage canals were the original prehistoric work and that the partially completed tunnels were part of the work designed by Crates.

When Xerxes led the army against the Greeks, he dug a canal across the isthmus of Mt. Athos and swung a bridge of boats across the Hellespont. The canal was about a mile and a half long, with the deepest cutting about fifty feet; a great deal of trouble was experienced in the cutting because some of the inexperienced workmen persisted in digging the trench with vertical sides which were continually falling in. The canal seems to have been quite useless after all, for Herodotus says that it would have been less trouble for Xerxes to have hauled his ships across the isthmus. This was done at the isthmus of Corinth, where the Greeks had talked for many years of building a canal and where they had made several futile attempts at construction, the last being in the time of Nero. The Corinthian canal was finally constructed in 1893, and is about four miles long.

The bridge of boats across the Hellespont was about a mile long; just as the work was completed a violent storm arose, breaking the moorings and destroying the bridge. The king was so enraged that he ordered the Hellespont to be chained and given three hundred lashes, and he had the engineers executed. This disciplinary action was so effective that, when the reconstruction of the bridge was undertaken by a new corps of engineers, the project was successfully completed; the engineers used stronger cables, and the chastened Hellespont preserved its calm.

Other examples of very early engineering works might be added. Ruins of some of these are found where their ancient builders had lived; and some of them give evidence of great constructive ability. They serve chiefly to show how far the greater works of the Greeks and Romans excelled them. They have perished, like the nations that produced them, leaving no impress on succeeding civilizations.

III. THE GREEK AND ROMAN
ENGINEERS

THE difference in the mental characteristics of the Greeks and Romans is
well illustrated by the different atti-
tudes of the two peoples toward engineering.
The Greeks were theorists and many of the
professional engineers among the Romans were
Greeks. The Romans were the projectors and
administrators of great public works. Strabo,
himself a Greek of Asia Minor, contrasts the
aestheticism of the Greeks with the utilitarian-
ism of the Romans, saying that the Grecian
cities had flourished mainly on account of the
felicitous choice of location by their founders,
whereas the Romans were more concerned with
matters which the Greeks neglected, such as
paved streets and aqueducts supplying running
water even in the houses. It is said that in the
age of Pericles, when Athens was filled with
beautiful buildings, the Athenians had neglected to build a bridge over their little river, the
Cephissus, although one of the principal roads

leading to the city crossed it by a ford. The Romans learned geometry and surveying from the Greeks and became very skilful in the practical application of these arts, but they cared nothing for the theoretical geometry in which the Greeks were so proficient. As Cicero said so well:

"In summo apud illos honore geometria fuit, itaque nihil mathematicis inlustrius; at nos metiendi ratiocinandique utilitate huius artis terminavimus modum." (*Tusc. Disp.*, I. 2. 5).

In short, geometry enjoyed an honorable position among them (i.e., the Greeks) and therefore no study was more brilliantly pursued than mathematics; but we have limited this art to the practical uses of measurement and surveying (calculation).

The earliest writer on engineering subjects whose writings have been preserved was Hero, an Alexandrian Greek of the second century B.C.

Hero is principally remembered as the inventor of the little reaction steam engine, known by his name, in which an escaping jet of steam caused the apparatus to rotate; he also devised a heat engine, operated by the expansive force of heated air, that could be used for opening doors and for performing other light work. Hero was a follower of Ctesibius, and some have claimed that he might perhaps have been his pupil. Ctesibius was one of the most celebrated of the Grecian engineers, and was the inventor of a two-cylinder force pump, which Vitruvius describes under the name of the *Ctesibica machina*. Hero described it in his *Pneumatica*. It consisted of two single-acting cylinders of bronze, fitted with pistons connected to a hand lever; the water was lifted by atmospheric pressure and then forced by the downward stroke of the piston into the air chamber and thence into the discharge pipe; the principle of construction and the operation of the apparatus being precisely like that of the hand fire engines used by the volunteer fire companies in the early part of the last century. Vitruvius' description, in part, follows:

"Next I must tell you about the machine of Ctesibius, which raises water to a height. It is made of bronze and has at the bottom a pair of cylinders set a little way apart, and there is a pipe connected with each, the two running up, like prongs of a fork, side by side to a vessel which is between the cylinders. In this vessel are valves, accurately fitting over the upper vents of the pipes, which stop up the ventholes, and keep what has been forced by pressure into the vessel from going down again. . . . Pistons smoothly turned, rubbed with oil, and inserted from above into the cylinders, work with their rods and levers upon the air and water in the cylinders, and, as the valves stop up the openings, force and drive the water, by repeated pressure and expansion, through the vents of the pipes into the vessel, from which the cowl receives the inflated currents, and sends them up through the pipe at the top; and so water can be supplied for a fountain from a reservoir at a lower level." (*Vitruvius*, tr. by M. H. Morgan, 1914, x, Chapter 7.)

The remains of a pump of this kind were found near Civita Vecchia in 1795. Another, found in Etruria, is now in the British Museum, and a third was found on the site of an old Roman cemetery near Metz in 1906. In the latter, the cylinders were of lead encased in a block of wood. Some of the valves and a part of one of the pistons were found.

Hero was the author of several books on mechanics and geometry; in the *Pneumatica* he describes the various applications of his hot air engine. Of special interest to the engineer is his *Dioptra*, which, besides containing a description of the engineering field instrument called by that name, is a practical treatise on surveying and engineering field work. In it he explains the process of levelling, how to ascertain the distance of an inaccessible point such as the width of a river, how to direct the alignment of tunnels, and he discusses other engineering field problems; he also treats of odometers and discusses the measurement of distances on the earth's surface, following the circumference of a great circle.

The instrument called the *dioptra,* from which the book takes its name, was a combined levelling and alignment instrument, foreshadowing, in principle, the modern theodolite. It consisted of a hollow cylindrical column of brass, about three feet in height, resting on three projecting points at the base, by which it was fixed in position on the ground; the column was made vertical by means of a plumbline. On the top of the column was fastened a horizontal plate carrying a vertical spindle, about which turned a second cylinder about a foot in diameter; to this second cylinder was fastened a toothed wheel by means of which it could be turned in azimuth and held in position by a tangent screw attached to the hori-

zontal plate. This second cylinder, which
rotated in azimuth, carried, on a horizontal axis,
a straight edge about six feet long, which could
be moved in altitude by means of a vertical
semi-circular plate, fixed to the horizontal axis,
operated and held in position by a tangent
screw; the straight edge was provided with a
water-level, and had at each end a thin plate,
slotted, to serve as sights. Except for the inaccuracy of the centering, the absence of any
means of adjustment, and the lack of precision
in the movements, it is evident that vertical and
horizontal angles could be laid off and measured, and the instrument used for the projection of alignment and for levelling; but its use
must have been attended with great inaccuracy.
There appears to have been no attempt to
divide the vertical and horizontal circles into
degrees for the direct measurement of angles;
in azimuth the right angle points were marked,
and other angles were probably measured by
off-sets on the perpendicular, or by measuring
the chords. Imperfect as it was, the *Dioptra*
contained in germ the principles on which modern surveying instruments are constructed, and
we must allow to Hero the distinction of making, or at least describing, the first reaction

steam engine, the first hot air engine, and the first theodolite.

Besides Frontinus, who wrote of the Aqueducts, the only Roman writer on engineering whose works have been preserved was Vitruvius, who is believed to have served as a military engineer under Julius Caesar and to have written his *Ten Books on Architecture* during the reign of Augustus.

Few professional writings have exerted so great influence on the practitioners of the art as the *De Architectura,* and few have been the subject of such careful study; upon the invention of printing, it was one of the first books to be published, three editions being included among the *incunabula.* During the Renaissance it was the handbook of all the great architects and engineers of the period.

The editio princeps was published in 1486 at Rome, with reprints in 1496 and 1497 at Florence and Venice; there were nine editions of the Latin text in the sixteenth century, besides five translations in Italian, two in French, and two in German. In 1673 was published the monumental French translation by the celebrated physician and architect, Claude Perrault, at the command and expense of Louis XIV;

this translation was republished with magnificent illustrations in 1684. In England, the Latin text was published in 1750; and translations by Newton in 1771, republished in 1791; by Wilkins in 1812, republished in 1817; and by Gwilt in 1874. A new translation by Professor Morgan of Harvard University appeared in 1914.

The portions of the work which treat of civil engineering are the fifth chapter of the first book, on *city walls;* the second book, which treats of *building materials and methods of construction;* parts of the eighth book, on *levelling* and the *construction of aqueducts;* and parts of the tenth book, on *hoisting engines* and *engines for raising water.* Vitruvius describes the qualifications of the successful architect, the necessity of combining both theory and practice. He insists on the importance of a liberal education, which was to include knowledge of geometry and drawing, of history, philosophy, music, medicine, the principles of law, and astronomy. His conception of the function of the architect was of the highest and reminds one of Hippocrates' exalted conception of medicine. " As for philosophy, it makes an architect high-minded and not self-assuming, but rather renders him courteous, just, and honest without avariciousness."

Philosophia vero perficit architectum animo magno et ut non sit adrogans, sed potius facilis aequus et fidelis sine avaritia, quod est maximum, nullum enim opus vere sine fide et castitate fieri potest.

" Consequently, since this study is so vast in extent, embellished and enriched as it is with many different kinds of learning, I think that men have no right to profess themselves architects hastily; without having climbed from boyhood the steps of these studies and thus, nursed by the knowledge of many arts and sciences, having reached the heights of the holy ground of architecture." (*Vitruvius,* tr. by M. H. Morgan, 1914. 1, Chapter 1.) He distinguishes between the elevation and plan and the drawing in perspective, where the lines " meet at the centre," or as we would say, at the vanishing point.

In describing the instruments used in levelling, Vitruvius enumerates the *Libra Aquaria* or water balance, the *Dioptra,* and the *Chorobates.* The *Dioptra* was, no doubt, Hero's instrument; the *Libra,* as the name indicates, was probably a straightedge in the form of a balance, with the sighting arm levelled by a water tube, as the *Dioptra* was, or it may have been a T-shaped instrument, with the longer arm weighted so that if suspended like a balance the cross arm would be level if truly set at right angles with the vertical arm. The *Libra* was also called *Libella*, the origin of our word "level." Vitruvius condemns them both and prefers the *Chorobates*. This he describes as a straightedge, about twenty feet long, with legs of equal length at each end, braced by cross pieces, on which vertical lines were marked at right angles to the straightedge; the coincidence of these lines with plumblines suspended from the straightedge indicated that the instrument was level. For use when a strong wind interfered with the vertical position of the plumblines, a groove, five feet long, was made on the straightedge to be filled with water, the instrument being considered level when the water uniformly filled the groove to its rims. Vitruvius here remarks that "readers of Archimedes" may object that there can be no true levelling by means of water, because Archimedes taught that water has a spherical surface with its center at the center of the earth, and

consequently could not be level; and he meets
this objection by the assertion that whether the
water be plane or spherical, it would still indicate a level line when it reached the same height
at the two ends of the groove, even if it " must
have a swelling and curvature in the centre."

The instrument ordinarily used for laying
out land lines was called the *Groma;* it consisted of two straight edges joined together at
right angles, pivoted at the center, and supported by a framework, or staff, in such a way
that the center of the *Groma* could be set vertically over a given point. From the ends of the
two crosspieces plumblines were suspended for
use in setting the instrument, and perhaps also
for sighting. If this instrument were properly
constructed and set, and carefully used, right
angles could be set off with sufficient accuracy
for the purposes for which it would ordinarly
be used.[2]

In the chapter on aqueducts, all the early
editions of Vitruvius, following the Editio
Princeps, read that the descending grade of an
aqueduct should not be less than one-half foot
in one hundred feet. Lanciani and Morgan,
following Rose's text, read " one-quarter of an
inch for every one hundred feet." This is the

same as given by Pliny, and is undoubtedly the correct reading. Vitruvius can hardly be supposed to prescribe, as a minimum, a gradient far in excess of the established practice of his time.

Notwithstanding the imperfections of their instruments, field work was generally well done. The Romans were accustomed to drive their tunnels from both ends, and expected the drifts to meet with a fair amount of precision; as for instance in the three-mile tunnel at Monte Affliano, on the line of the Claudian aqueduct, where the tunnel was only three feet wide. One case is recorded where the opposing drifts missed each other entirely. The engineer was Nonius Datus, an engineer attached to the Third Legion. After carefully surveying and marking the line, he was called away, presumably in military service. During his absence, the tunnels passed the expected meeting point, and Nonius was hurriedly summoned to investigate and advise what should be done. In his report, he states that as usual the blame was put on the engineer, although the fault was really with the contractor, who in producing the alignment had in both cases deviated to the right, so that if Nonius had not been sent for, there would have been two tunnels instead of one. Fortunately the tunnel was for an aqueduct and not for a railroad, and Nonius was able to locate a transverse tunnel connecting the two, and so the work was satisfactorily completed.

The Roman engineers generally displayed great ingenuity in the location of their work; they fitted the lines of their aqueducts to the contour of the ground and selected favorable points for crossing the valleys, thus reducing the length of their bridges. While some of their arches and piers approximate in their dimensions to modern practice, they ordinarily made up for their lack of theoretical knowledge by an excessive use of material, building short spans with heavy piers. Occasionally when building on firm ground they adopted a bolder design with longer spans, especially at river crossings when by so doing they could avoid a pier in midstream. Leger commends them for this, saying that in systematically exaggerating the solidity of their construction, they made no mistake; and it is due to the massive construction of the piers of the aqueducts that so many of those great arches are still standing on the Roman Campagna.

IV. MATERIALS AND METHODS OF CONSTRUCTION

THE development of a constructive art is largely dependent upon the availability of suitable material, and in this respect the Roman engineers were especially favored in the abundant supply of easily dressed and durable stone which they found in Rome and the neighboring country.

The principal materials used in the public works of Rome were as follows. Although these have been discussed in many places,[3] a brief consideration of them is desirable here. Tufa is the name, used today, of the stone which Vitruvius calls *Ruber et niger tofus.* (Vitruvius, II. 7. 1.) There are many varieties of this stone, which may be described as a volcanic conglomerate of scoriae, ashes, and sand. In places this stone is friable and so loosely compacted that it can be easily dug into with a spade; elsewhere, it has been hardened by time and pressure, but even so, it remains a comparatively soft stone, which could be quarried with bronze implements. It varies in colors, described as reddish brown, gray-green or greenish-yellow, called *cappellacio* (which is very poor), and deep brown. This stone existed in quantities in all of the hills of Rome. The Palatine tufa tells the tale of showers of hot ashes that had fallen on a forest of trees, as large lumps of charcoal are embedded in this tufa rock and these resulted from smothering of the burning wood from ashes. The Capitoline quarries lay on the eastern slope of the Capitoline hill, back of the Tullianum, and constituted the well-known Lautumiae. The Quirinal, Esquiline, and Aventine hills also furnished this building material for Rome. Outside of Rome are the great quarries known as the *Grotte della Cervara*, at the fifth milestone of the Via Collatina. On the right bank of the Tiber, south of the Janiculan hill, are the quarries of brown tufa now called *Monte Verde*. This superior variety of tufa also lies along the Anio. It was used in Rome even before the close of the regal period, while after the middle of the fourth century B.C., the yellowish Etruscan tufa of *Grotta Oscura* became popular. Tufa was employed in the regal period, during the Republic till the Augustan age, and even in the Empire period.

We find the different varieties of tufa in the "Walls of Romulus," the "Servian" Wall, in the podia of the Capitoline temple (of the sixth century), of the temples of Saturn and of Castor (of the fifth century), and tufa was used as a space-filler in concrete walls of the Empire. After the middle of the second century B.C., a variety of brown tufa became the regular building material for ordinary masonry. It was quarried on the Palatine, the Capitoline, and the Aventine hills, at Monte Verde, all along the Anio, and especially at Cervara. All varieties of tufa weathered badly and required a protection or covering of stucco. Pliny is most uncomplimentary: tofus aedificiis inutilis est mortalitate, mollitia. (*N.H.*, xxxvi. 22. 48. 166.)

But better than tufa was another stone of two varieties, which came into common use in the third century B.C. This stone was much harder and resulted from the action of hot water upon a conglomerate of volcanic ashes, gravel, and sand. Of the two varieties, one was called lapis Albanus and the other, lapis Gabinus. The lapis Albanus, quarried in the Alban Hills, was only a moderately good weather stone but was quite fireproof. It contains scoriae in large number and as these resemble peppercorns it has been called "peperino." This designation is at least as old as the sixth century, as it is found in the *Etymologiae* of Isidorus:

Albus lapis, alius durus, alius mollis . . .
Piperinus, subalbidus cum punctis nigris,
durus etque fortissimus. (*Etym.*, xix. 10. 8.)

It was employed in the " Servian " Wall, and in the Claudian aqueduct; quarries at Albano and Marino still supply Italians today with this building material. Lapis Gabinus, quarried at ancient Gabii, is called " sperone " today. It is still harder than lapis Albanus and is a better weather stone, as is admirably illustrated by the surrounding wall of the Forum of Augustus. The lower part of this wall, constructed of lapis Gabinus, remains fresh and intact, whereas the upper portion, built of lapis Albanus, has weathered badly. Lapis Gabinus was employed in the façade of the Tabularium (first century B.C.). The reputation of these two building materials is shown clearly by the remark of Tacitus who says that after the great conflagration in A.D. 64, Nero directed thƨt buildings should be raised for a

certain portion of their height without beams
and arched with Gabine or Alban stone, which
was fireproof:

aedificiaque ipsa certa sui parte sine trabibus saxo
Gabino Albanove solidarentur, quod is lapis igni-
bus impervius est. (*Annales,* xv. 43.)

Strabo says that at Gabii, there was a rock-
quarry more serviceable to Rome than any
other: Γάβιοι, .. λατόμιον ἔχουσα ὑπουργὸν τῇ
Ῥώμῃ μάλιστα τῶν ἄλλων. (v. 3. 10.)

More useful than lapis Albanus or lapis
Gabinus was lapis Tibertinus, which derived
its name from the principal quarries that lay
near Tibur, now called Tivoli. These quarries
and the method of extracting this stone have
been fascinatingly described by Lanciani.
The quarries are reached by going to Aquae
Albulae, on the Tivoli line, where the sulphur
springs, of ancient and modern renown, are
located. From the sulphur springs an aqueduct, running parallel with an ancient road, led
to the quarries and supplied the motive power
for extracting the stone. The quarries were
of immense size and it has been estimated that
over five million cubic metres of stone were
taken from this source. Broken chips were

transported to a distance, as far as the banks
of the Anio, and piled up in a chain of artificial hills that remind us of Monte Testaccio
at Rome. Vitruvius (II. 7. 2.) describes lapis
Tiburtinus, or " travertine " as it is now called,
as an excellent weather-stone but as easily
calcined by fire:

Tiburtina vero et quae eodem genere sunt omnia
sufferunt et ab oneribus et a tempestatibus iniurias,
sed ab igni non possunt esse tuta simulque sunt ab
eo tacta dissiliunt et dissipantur.

But travertine and all stones of that class can
stand injury, whether from a heavy load laid upon
it or from the weather; exposure to fire, however,
it cannot bear, but splits and cracks to pieces at
once (Morgan's translation).

Pliny's statement is very similar:

Tiburtini (lapides) ad reliqua fortes vapore dissiliunt. (*N. H.*, xxxvi. 22. 48. 167.)

When burnt, as the carbonic acid gas is
driven off, it produces excellent lime, and this
lime, combined with sand and gravel, was later
employed in making concrete, cement, and
mortar. But travertine " is an almost pure
carbonate of lime, very hard, of a beautiful

creamy colour, which weathers into a rich golden tint. It is a deposit from running water, and is formed in a highly stratified state, with frequent cavities and fissures, lined with crystallized carbonate of lime." It proved strong if laid on its natural bed, but otherwise its use involved dangerous results. During the second half of the second century B.C. and after, travertine became the great building material of Rome. At first it was used sparingly, especially in members subject to stress or at exposed points, such as keystones of arches, capitals, architraves, cornices, or stylobates. The Mulvian bridge (109 B.C.) furnishes us with the first known example of its use in large structures, but even here, though used with knowledge of its strength for wearing and carrying purposes, it is used with caution. The Fabrician bridge was built in 62 B.C., but it was built of tufa and peperino, with only facings of travertine. It appears that it was not until 42 B.C. that travertine was employed freely, in the rebuilding of the temple of Saturn. The existing podium belongs to that date. In the Augustan age, this stone was used extensively, as, for example, in the Basilica Aemilia and the Theatre of Marcellus, the temple of Castor, and the "House of Livia." As is well known, travertine contributed mightily to the "Eternal City," and one of the most conspicuous illustrations of its use is in the Colosseum. Once its value was recognized, it was employed in preference to peperino, wherever greater strength was required, as for keystones or for the imposts and voussoirs of arches; for example, the voussoirs of the Arco dei Pantani, within the surrounding wall of the Forum of Augustus, are of travertine. Employed in St. Peter's, it has also been used in the interior of the general waiting room of the Pennsylvania Terminal in New York City and in many other public buildings.

Silex (the modern " Selce ") is often erroneously understood to be flint, but it is in reality lava, which came to Rome from the craters of the Sabatine range and, especially, in four streams from the Alban volcanoes. As is well known, the tomb of Caecilia Metella, one of the commanding monuments of the Campagna, stands at the edge of one of these streams, marking the point, about three miles from Rome, which this stream had reached. It is a very hard stone, described by Vitruvius, and by Pliny the Elder (*N.H.*, xxxvi. 22. 49. 168), and it was particularly serviceable in the pavements of streets, where large blocks, pentagonal in shape, were employed. Smaller pieces, combined with pozzolana and lime, added to the strength of concrete and rubble. Storehouses, which perhaps also served as barracks for workmen on the road, were called *castra silicariorum* (barracks of the Silicarii).

As is well known, there are no examples in Rome of cyclopean or polygonal masonry, i.e., of walls built of blocks of stone of irregular shape. The earliest walls known are built of rectangular blocks of stone, laïd in regular courses. Such masonry appears in the fragments of the so-called " Wall of Romulus," in the " Servian " Wall, in the foundations of the Jupiter Capitoline temple, and in the façade of the Tabularium. This method of building was called opus quadratum by the Romans (cf. Vitruvius, ii. 8. 1–8) and it continued in use until at least the third century after Christ. In standard construction, rectangular blocks of stone (i.e. of tufa or peperino) were used, two Roman feet in height and two in thickness, and four feet long. These were laid in alternate courses of headers and stretchers, i.e. length-

wise and endwise, in a method called " emplec-
ton." Of course tufa was first employed, and
peperino, which appears in the Wall of Servius
Tullius, later, yet comparatively early. Travertine, as we have learned, came into use in the
latter part of the second century before Christ.
Blocks of this stone were not all of the same
size, as it was not so easily worked. The finest
example in Rome of a solid travertine wall is
found in the wall of the podium of the temple
of Vespasian. Here the massive blocks are
perfectly jointed, and the iron cramps, used to
hold the blocks together in theoretically greater
security, are entirely unnecessary. In the case
of the podium of the temple of Faustina, we
find another striking example of extraordinary
workmanship, where the beds and joints are
dressed so accurately that the joints are hardly
perceptible. The blocks, of peperino in this
case, are so exquisitely jointed that this work
has been compared to the perfection of the
work of Greek builders who laid drums of marble upon one another with perfect accuracy.
Another excellent specimen of opus quadratum
work is found in the front of the Tabularium
(78 B.C.). In inner walls of the Colosseum,
tufa, peperino, and travertine are all em-

ployed, but in such cases the harder stone is regularly used for keystones and voussoirs, i.e. wherever there was the greatest pressure. This is well illustrated by the surrounding wall of the Forum of Augustus; the voussoirs of the Arco dei Pantani, the entrance archway by which the Forum is still entered, are of travertine, while lapis Albanus and lapis Gabinus are employed elsewhere. Travertine is also used in a projecting course, at intervals of fifteen courses.

Mortar was, perhaps, used between blocks of stone, in opus quadratum masonry, even early, but the thin bed of lime was not intended as a binding material, but simply to render the joints more perfect. It is thought by some that " mortar " was not employed in Italy before the third century B.C. But toward the close of the Republic and early in the Empire, mortar was used infrequently. The surfaces of stone blocks were made so smooth, that accurate fitting resulted. In spite of this the Romans had recourse to the use of iron cramps, and wooden dowels, on occasion, to render the work even more secure. Vitruvius' statement about iron cramps deserves quotation:

et cum his ansis ferreis et plumbo frontes vinctae sint (II. 8. 4.),

i.e. the cramps were fastened with molten lead.[4]
Horace doubtless had the practice in mind,
when he wrote:

Te *semper anteit saeva Necessitas,*
Clavos trabalis et cuneos manu
Gestans aëna, nec severus
Uncus abest liquidumque plumbum.

Smeaton followed the Roman practice in building the Eddystone lighthouse, using wooden
wedges to tighten the dovetails by which the
stones in each course were locked together.
Opus quadratum masonry yielded only to concrete construction, of which a word should
be said.

The discovery of the availability and possible
uses of " pozzolana " (as it is called today) was
of epochal importance in the history of Roman
building. Great beds of this volcanic ash (or
sand) lie near Naples at Puteoli (now called
Pozzuoli), whence the ancient name of pulvis
Puteolanus. It also existed in enormous quantities on the hills underneath Rome and in the
Campagna, about Rome, where it was de-
posited, as showered down by very ancient volcanic activity. There it lay in two strata, an
upper stratum of light gray ash, and a

lower stratum, deeper down, darker in color, chocolate-red, and possessing greater binding quality. Once the great value of this volcanic earth or ash had been learned, it not only superseded the earlier varieties of sands used in making mortar, but, in particular, contributed to the concrete which truly made Rome the "Eternal City."

Three kinds of sands (arenae) were known to the Romans (Vitruvius, II. 4.): arena fossitia or pit-sand, which was the best, and of which an excellent variety, sharp, clean, and golden, lay on the Janiculan Hill; arena de fluminibus, or river-sand, such as the Tiber furnished, not so good in character, because of the impurities it contained; and arena marina, or sea-sand, also defective, because of the admixture of salt (Vitruvius, II. 4. 2.). While sand and lime had earlier been employed as a mortar, we find pulvis Puteolanus (or volcanic ash) mixed with lime, as a mortar-lining of the water channel (specus) of the Aqua Marcia as early as 144 B.C. Although Cato (*De Agricultura*, 18.7) knew how *cement* could be made of "pulvis Puteolanus" and lime, it was not until the first century B.C. that experimentation had passed into established usage and that the great and daring results in the form of walls (as of the Pantheon, nearly twenty feet thick), vaults and domes appeared, and that structura cae- menticia (or "concrete," as we call it) trans- formed Roman building methods. In the podium of the temple of Concord (120 B.C.), we find the first known example of its use at Rome. In the making of this "concrete" (or "cement"), the Romans added to the mixture of "pulvis Puteolanus" and lime, broken frag- ments of stone, such as tufa, at first, then peper- ino, and later in the Empire, travertine and silex, not to mention broken bits of brick, pot- tery, and of marble; lumps of pumice stone were employed, when lightness was desired, as in arched vaults. This cement was of extraor- dinary strength, setting hard even under water. Vitruvius' words are well known:

quod cum commixtum cum calce et caemento non modo ceteris aedificiis praestat firmitatem, sed etiam moles cum struuntur in mari, sub aqua solidescunt. (II. 6. I.)

To the discovery of this "concrete" the Romans owed their great triumphs, such as the dome of the Pantheon, and the great vaults that appear in the Thermae, and in the Basilica of

Constantine. Lacking the great lateral thrust of the stone arch, these superb roofings are rigid, yet rest, comparatively lightly, upon the supporting walls. None before the Romans had so used concrete, and modern engineering has but recently followed their example, the great advance in modern practice being due to improved methods of manufacture and the use of metallic reinforcements. When building walls of concrete, the Romans poured the mixture in a semi-fluid state and allowed it to set within a framework of timbers, which then was removed as the wall was raised to a higher level. Marks left in the soft concrete by the boarding still appear in the face of the concrete of the foundations of the Flavian palace on the Palatine. Such concrete was also poured within surrounding walls of stone, making a solid podium foundation for temple structures, as, for example, in the reconstruction of the temples of Saturn and of Castor. In walls of considerable thickness, the Romans occasionally built face walls of opus quadratum and filled the space between them with concrete. Vitruvius (II. 8. 7.) finds fault with this, preferring the methods of the Greeks, who, he says, built their walls of solid stone, laying every stone level, with headers extending through from face to face; but, as he says, the Romans after building the facing walls, filled the space between them with concrete or rubble, thus making three sections of different compressive strength in the same structure; danger lay, to be sure, in the use of loose rubble, but Vitruvius had not learned the strength of Roman concrete, when he wrote. Modern builders still employ pozzolana in making ordinary mortars, deriving it from pits in the Campagna. Smeaton, pioneer of the great English engineers, used pozzolana cement in the construction of the Eddystone lighthouse.

Concrete walls, except in foundations, were regularly faced in Rome and the designations of opus incertum, opus reticulatum, opus testaceum or latericium, and opus mixtum are given to the various kinds of facings, which require a word of explanation. Opus incertum (Vitruvius, II. 8. i.) consisted of irregular bits of tufa, — their outer surface dressed smooth, — conical or pyramidal in shape, which tailed into the concrete wall behind. This was the earliest form of facing and one of the earliest examples of its use is found in the second century concrete wall, at the foot of the Scalae Caci on the Palatine Hill. Opus incertum was in vogue during the second and first centuries before Christ, and an excellent example of its use is to be found in the outer wall of the little round temple at Tibur (Tivoli). Opus reticulatum superseded it in the first century B.C. and continued in use during the first two centuries after Christ. It seems to have been introduced in the time of Sulla, and examples of it are very numerous, appearing, for example, in the "House of Livia" on the Palatine Hill and, later, in Hadrian's villa at Tivoli. In Rome, tufa blocks were employed exclusively. Tufa prisms, of regular pyramid shape, were so carefully set to run in diagonal lines that their exterior facing presented the appearance of the neatest meshes of network, from which the name of opus reticulatum was derived. Of course these facings had no (or very little) structural value and were not employed in arch work or at angles of walls. Opus reticulatum often appears in great panels, four to five feet high, on the outer surface of concrete walls. One is amazed at the waste of energy and skill in setting such facings, upon reflection that a stucco covering ordinarily hid them from view. Vitruvius' words (II. 8. 1.)

call attention to the wide use of this kind of facing:

structurarum genera sunt haec, reticulatum quo nunc omnes utuntur, et antiquum, quod incertum dicitur.

As early as the first century B.C. brick facing was also employed and it continued to the end of the Western Empire. Bricks, so employed, varied in size and shape, but it was the triangular brick that was most commonly used, as a facing in walls of concrete. Square and rectangular bricks and tiles were used in the facings of vaults and arches, and at corners, and also as bonding courses. It is important to remember that sun-dried bricks (lateres crudi) may have been extensively used earlier in the Republic; but no specimens of such bricks have survived. During the first century B.C., however, kiln-baked bricks (lateres cocti) and tiles (testae, tegulae) were made, and it is these that concern us here. Lanciani has given an intensely interesting sketch of the history of brick-making in Rome, calling attention to the shapes of bricks, the seals and symbols that appear upon them, the profits in brick-making, and the exportation of bricks to remote places in the Empire. Bricks found in England have the same hardness as those in Rome, much harder than modern bricks made of the same clay. In fact, Roman burnt bricks, found in England, are so hard that they strike fire like a flint. It is well to recall Vitruvius' exhortation:

maxime autem utiliores erunt, si ante biennium fuerint ducti. Namque non ante possunt penitus siccescere. (II. 3. 2)

Hilaire Belloc declares that the uniformity of Roman bricks, whether found in Britain or on the banks of the Euphrates, is one of the most impressive indications of the unity and extent of the Roman Empire. While walls may have been built of bricks before the first century B.C., it was only as a facing that the bricks were used later. In the time of Nero and the early years of the Flavian Emperors we find the best examples of opus testaceum. In such work the brick is comparatively thick, with only a thin bed of mortar or cement; but as time goes on, the reverse is true; the brick becomes thinner and the bed of mortar thicker, as we see in the walls of Aurelian, where bricks and joints are about equal in thickness. One of the finest examples of brick-work in Rome is to be seen

in the arches of Nero's extension of the Claudian Aqueduct on the Caelian hill, although
perhaps later than Nero. In the third century
A.D., a new type of facing comes into use which
has been called opus mixtum; this facing consists of a mixture of opus testaceum, followed
at irregular intervals by a facing of rectangular
tufa blocks, and it proclaims the deterioration
of older styles. It appears in the Circus of
Maxentius, of A.D. 310.

Plaster or stucco (tectorium) covered all of
these facings, as a rule. (Vitruvius, VII. 2–6.)
It was used as a covering not only in the case
of facings of concrete walls but even, at times,
of opus quadratum masonry. Two kinds of
plaster or stucco deserve especial attention:
opus signinum, which consisted of lime and pozzolana, combined with pounded bits of brick or
pottery, hence also called opus e testis tunsis;
this was especially valuable as a lining of the
water-channels of aqueducts and in cisterns;
the other variety was called opus albarium or
caementum marmoreum. This consisted of
lime, powdered white marble, water or milk,
some albuminous or glutinous substance such
as the white of eggs or the sap of the fig-tree.
It was applied even to marble surfaces,

was capable of high polish, and could hold pigments.

The use of broken pottery for concrete was common among the Romans, and of this material they possessed an inexhaustible supply. They used pottery for all kinds of containers, they stored their wine in jars instead of casks, and the wheat of Egypt was loaded on the ships in earthenware *dolia*. Immense heaps of broken pottery are found in many places, and near the wharves on the Tiber, just below the old city, there is a hill, the "Monte Testaccio," a half mile in circumference and over a hundred feet high, composed entirely of broken jars.

The use of marbles in Rome was responsible for the great transformation of the city, recorded in the famous boast of Augustus:

urbem, neque pro maiestate imperii ornatam et inundationibus incendiisque obnoxiam, excoluit adeo, ut iure sit gloriatus marmoream se relinquere, quam latericiam accepisset (Suet., *Aug.*, 28.)

Crassus, the orator, adorned his home on the Palatine with columns of Hymettian marble and as this seemed an absurd novelty in his day (about 92 B.C.), he was called in ridicule the "Palatine Venus" (Pliny, *N.H.*, XXXVI. 3. 3.

7.). Horace disclaimed any intention of employing the luxury of marbles in his home.

> *Non ebur neque aureum*
>   *Mea renidet in domo lacunar,*
> *Non trabes Hymettiae*
>   *Premunt columnas ultima recisas*
> *Africa,* ....*(Odes,* 11. 18. 1–5.)

It was in the first century B.C. that the use of marbles, as building material, began in Rome, but in the Empire period it has been estimated that no less than one hundred and fifty varieties were known.

The following kinds of this stone deserve mention even in a brief sketch:

Pentelic, pure white, and of very fine grain;
Hymettian, with bluish gray veins;
Parian, of coarser grain and strongly crystalline, — all three, of course, imported from Greek lands;
Luna marble, quarried near Carrara, of many varieties, one being a pure ivory white;
Numidian, called giallo antico, a rich golden or pale yellow marble, often with veins of orange and pink, obtained from Africa;
Phrygian, called pavonazetto, from its darker

purple markings, with veins of white, re-
minding one of the peacock's colors.

Juvenal satirizes the extravagant use of marble in his day and says:

Cretonius was a great builder; now on the curved
shore of Caieta, now on Tibur's highest peak, now
on Praeneste's Hills he prepared him lofty villas
with marbles brought from Greece and far away,
surpassing the magnificence of Fortuna's temple
and of Hercules . . . But his mad son has squan-
dered all his property, while rearing new villas of
even more costly marbles. (*Sat.*, XIV. 86–95.)

Carystian, called cipollino, from its onion-like
waves of white and pale green, was a highly
stratified marble, quarried at Carystos in
Euboea, — the *undosa Carystos* of Statius
(*Silvae*, 1. 5. 36); the columns of the temple
of Antoninus and Faustina are of this marble;
Rosso antico, a deep red marble, from Greece,
highly decorative in character, and employed
in cornices and architraves;
Nero antico, black in color, generally with white
veins, also brought from Greece;
Hard volcanic stones: granite, red and gray,
from Naxos and Egypt; examples in the
columns of the Temple of Saturn and the

Portico of the Pantheon; red porphyry from Egypt, and green from Lacedaemon; basalt, black, brown, and dark green in color; verde antico, "serpentine," dull green in color, from Thessaly. Alabaster, from Egypt and Arabia, added to the brilliancy of the imperial capital.

These and many more varieties of marble and of other valuable stones, employed in the making of statues, in columns, floors, wall-linings and decorations, justified the boast of Augustus, which was even more prophecy than description of the city of his day. Rarely were solid blocks of marble used in the construction of a wall, as was the case with the restoration of the Regia, in 36 B.C., but it was as a facing to walls of concrete that slabs of marble were so extensively employed. Great wharves for the reception of imported marble slabs were developed along the Tiber, below the Aventine, and above the Pons Aelius, in the Campus Martius. We know the technical names of marble and stone masons, employed in various capacities, such as, *statuarii* or *fictores, sculptores, lapidarii, marmorarii, politores,* and *caesores;* mining engineers were called *machinarii.* Pliny (*N.H.,* xxxvi. 1–6 *seq.*) gives us an eloquent description of the use and abuse of all of these materials in Rome.

While the architecture of the Greeks was rectilinear architecture, in which direct vertical supports carried the horizontal members, the arch principle, the use of the vault and the dome, did not enter conspicuously into their buildings. The arch principle was known very early and was employed by the Hellenistic Greeks in substructures. The principle of the arch was known to the Etruscans, as we learn from their monumental gateways, and the vault and the dome were also familiar to them, as their rock-hewn tombs show. But it remained for the Romans to effect a revolution in principles of construction, by the use of curves. The arch, the vault, and the dome were carried forward to hitherto unknown triumphs, as in the Tabularium, the Pantheon, the Colosseum, the Thermae of Caracalla and of Diocletian, and in the Basilica of Constantine. A dome or cupola over a circular drum was, perhaps, less astonishing, but a dome over a rectangular space was amazing. In decoration the Romans showed less ingenuity. The Tuscan column, the Doric, the Ionic, and the Corinthian seemed to have exhausted all possibilities, and it remained, merely, for the Romans to add the Composite.

Skew arches were seldom used in stone masonry and only for small angles of skew; the Romans knew nothing of spiral or helicoidal courses, and their skew arches were treated precisely the same as right-angled arches, except that they occasionally attempted to relieve the unbalanced pressure at the ends of the arch by relieving arches of brick. The expedient of building arches in parallel rings does not appear to have been applied to skew arches of stone masonry, although occasionally used in rectangular arches, as in the Pont du Gard, and in constructions of concrete. Occasionally these double arch rings were at some distance apart, the intervening space being afterwards covered by an arch ring of cut stone, or filled with a ring of concrete or rubble, as was done in the Pont St. Martin in the valley of Aosta and in the bridge of El-Kantara in Algeria.

Notwithstanding their skill in masonry construction, the Romans avoided the building of groined arches in stone masonry. When practicable they got rid of the intersection altogether by adjusting the levels of the intersecting vaults, so that the springing line of one would come above the crown of the other, or by terminating each gallery in a square chamber at the intersection; in other cases they formed the intersecting vaults of concrete. In the construction of concrete groined arches, it was quite common to throw light brick arches diagonally across the opening on the lines of the groins, using the brick arches as supports for the deposition of the concrete, simplifying the construction and economizing in the use of heavy centering; a similar practice was frequently followed in simple arches.

At Narnia, on the Flaminian Way, about forty miles from Rome, are ruins of an arched viaduct over the river Nar, the principal arch having a span of about one hundred and fifteen feet; the arch has fallen but portions of the piers and some of the imposts remain. Choisy is of the opinion that the fallen arch may have been an elliptical or perhaps a basket-handle arch, tilted, to rest on imposts of unequal heights; Leger, however, represents the arch as a full-centered semicircular arch, which corresponds better with the usual Roman practice; there is perhaps too little left of the structure to determine this point with certainty.

A characteristic feature of Roman construction is their economy in the use of scaffolding and centering. Besides the square holes in the walls which Choisy believes indicate the places where beams were inserted to support the scaffolding, it was customary to build stone corbels in the walls for the same purpose, and in the larger arches the second or third voussoir was extended within the intrados to support the centers for the remaining portion of the arch. These projecting voussoirs are conspicuous in the Pont du Gard.

The hoisting machines used by the Romans for lifting heavy blocks of stone are described by Vitruvius in the second chapter of his tenth book. For ordinary use, two timbers were set up, bolted together at the top and spread apart at the bottom, the whole being held in position by guy ropes attached to the top. From the top a block was suspended with two sheaves, one above the other; the rope was reeved round the upper sheave, carried down and passed round the sheave of a single block below, then returned to the upper block, passed round its lower sheave and brought down to the lower block and fastened to it. The free end of the rope was carried to a windlass, the axle of which was supported by bearing pieces fastened to the back of the two main timbers. The windlass was turned by handspikes inserted in holes in the shaft. The stone was carried by tongs attached to the lower block, the prongs of which engaged in holes cut in the stone. Some editions of Vitruvius read three timbers instead of two, making a tripod instead of a sheers, with the same arrangement of tackle. Larger pulleys with three sheaves in the upper block and two in the lower block were also used.

For hoisting the heaviest stones the windlass was replaced by a large drum wheel, round which a rope was wound and carried to a capstan or to a treadmill. For such derricks the number of sheaves was doubled by placing others side by side in the same block and using two falls.

A single masted derrick was also used, guyed by ropes from the top. Three-fold pulleys were used, with three rows of sheaves, three in each row. Three fall ropes were attached to the upper block, reeved round the three sets of pulleys, and, returning from the top, were passed through a three-fold single pulley at the foot of the machine and thence were led to three gangs of laborers, who were often slaves or prisoners, pulling directly on the ropes. Rondelet states that derricks of this kind were used in his time at the seaports of France and Italy and in Paris.

V. THE AQUEDUCTS

PROCOPIUS, writing of the great bridge at Narnia, says that its "arches were built long ago and are the highest known." Likewise there are many allusions to the Roman aqueducts in the ancient literature, that are casual and incidental, as might be expected. Even in the chapter on "Marvellous Buildings in Rome," in which Pliny the Elder speaks of the Circus Maximus, basilicas, temples, fora, sewers, palaces, theatres, amphitheatres, harbors, etc., the account of the aqueducts is brief enough (Plin., *N.H.*, XXXVI. 15. 24. 101–125). Only three sections are devoted to the subject of aqueducts and the account is neither precise nor very original. He introduces his discussion, saying:

Sed dicantur vera aestumatione invicta miracula (§ 121),
but let us now discuss marvels which, if properly estimated, are unsurpassed,

and he mentions the Appian, the Anio, the Marcian, the Tepula, the Virgo, the Claudian aqueducts.

He adds: " But if anyone will note the abundance of water skilfully brought into the city, for public uses, for baths, for public basins, for houses, runnels, suburban gardens, and villas; if he will note the high aqueducts required for maintaining the proper elevation; the mountains which had to be pierced for the same reason and the valleys it was necessary to fill up; he will conclude that the whole terrestrial orb offers nothing more marvellous,"

fatebitur nihil magis mirandum fuisse in toto orbe terrarum (§ 123).

This but whets our appetite for fuller, detailed information. What would we not give for full technical accounts by contemporary engineers to supplement our knowledge of the ruins that have survived their handiwork ? Cicero, Livy, Tacitus, Dio Cassius, the poets, and, later, Ulpian and Cassiodorus refer to the aqueducts and give us bits of information. Inscriptions add greatly to our information. But it is to be regretted that the Roman engineers did not anticipate the example of Telford, who wrote an extensive autobiography with full descriptions of his bridges and highways. Agrippa was responsible for building the Pantheon, but we should like to know the name of the architect and possess his commentaries. Not even Agrippa has left us an account of the history of the building of the great temple that still bears his name.

In the thirty-first book of his *Natural History*, Pliny discusses many remarkable facts connected with water, as

> different properties of water,
> remedies derived from water,
> methods of searching for water,
> and the signs indicative of its presence,
> methods of conveying water, etc.

In the latter chapter he makes the observation that water always rises to the level of its source:

> Subit altitudinem exortus sui (**XXXI**. 6. 31. 57)

and Vitruvius is a most important source on many of these topics, as,

> how to find water,
> rain-water,
> various properties of different waters,
> tests of good water,
> levelling instruments,
> aqueducts, wells, and cisterns (Vitr., VIII).

In the case of the aqueducts, we are most fortunate in possessing the descriptions of the aqueducts of Rome, written by Sextus Julius Frontinus, who was *curator aquarum* or superintendent of the water supply of the city of Rome, appointed under Nerva, in A.D. 97. Frontinus was a man of great distinction, who served his state as praetor and consul, and as commander in Britain, where he gained an important victory over the Silures:

Iulius Frontinus, vir magnus . . . validamque et pugnacem Silurum gentem armis subegit, super virtutem hostium locorum quoque difficultates eluctatus (Tac., *Agr.*, 17).

Martial (X. 58) addressed an epigram to Frontinus. They had cultivated the Muses, together, at Baiae. Frontinus was a friend of Pliny the Younger, who was grateful for succeeding Frontinus in the college of augurs (*Ep.*, IV. 8. 3):

Mihi vero etiam illud gratulatione dignum videtur, quod successi Iulio Frontino, principi viro.

The work *De Aquis Urbis Romae,* in two books, was begun in Nerva's reign and completed under Trajan. The sole original manuscript (of the twelfth to fourteenth century) was discovered about A.D. 1400 in the library of the Benedictine monastery of Monte Cassino, by the great Poggio, who made eight copies of the original. The *editio princeps* appeared in 1484–92 and in the early days of printing it was customary to include the *De Aquis* with the *De Architectura* of Vitruvius. Frontinus shared with Vitruvius the vogue which the latter enjoyed among the architects and engineers of the Renaissance.

An early chapter of Frontinus sets forth his aims and gives us a fair survey of the subjects he discusses:

And that I may not by chance omit anything which is requisite for a comprehension of the whole subject, I shall discuss the

names of the waters brought to the city,

the persons who brought them and the dates,

the sources of the aqueducts and their lengths,

the underground channels, the masonry substructures, and the arches,

the height of the aqueducts,

the size and number of taps,

the amount of water conveyed by each aqueduct,

the delivery tanks and the distribution of the water within the city,

the construction and maintenance of the aqueducts. **(Introd., § 3)**

The first permanent *Curator Aquarum* was Marcus Vipsanius Agrippa (Front., II. 98), appointed to that office by the Emperor Augustus in 34 B.C. Agrippa was a confidential adviser of Augustus in the critical period following the assassination of Julius Caesar, and commanded his fleet at the battle of Actium. Besides being the constructor of several aqueducts, he was the builder of the original Pantheon, which was afterwards partially destroyed by fire and restored by Domitian, again destroyed, but reconstructed by Hadrian and finally rebuilt by Severus. The careers of such men as Agrippa and Frontinus illustrate the importance of the engineer among the Romans, and their appointment to the office of *Curator* shows the care that was taken to secure men of tried ability to fill important administrative positions.

When Frontinus wrote, there were nine aqueducts in service at Rome. Two others were afterwards added, making eleven in all. There are now four, the Vergine, Felice, Paola, and Pia or Marcia-Pia, which are duplicates or reconstructions of the ancient Virgo, Alexandrina, Alsietina and Trajana, and the Marcia, respectively.

The eleven aqueducts of old Rome, in the order of their construction, were as follows:

Aqua Appia. The first of the Roman aqueducts was constructed in 312 B.C., by Appius Claudius Caecus, who was also the builder of the Appian Way. Its source was from springs in the valley of the Anio, about seven miles from Rome; its total length was about ten miles, the increase in length being due to its following the contour of the ground, in order to maintain an approximately regular grade line. Except for a distance of a little less than three hundred feet, where it crossed the Appian Way on a line of low arches, outside the Porta Capena, it was entirely underground. Remains of this aqueduct have been found on the Aventine Hill, but the greater part of its course outside the city has not been traced. It approached the city near the temple of *Spes Vetus,* just outside the Porta Praenestina ("Maggiore," as it is called today) of the later Wall of Aurelian. It crossed the southern slope of the Caelian, crossed the valley of the Piscina Publica, i.e., between the Caelian and the Aventine, very near the Porta Capena (where it was carried on arches, as has been said), crossed the Aventine, near S. Saba, turned N.W. and ended not far from the foot of the Clivus Publicius, near the Porta Trigemina.

Incipit distribui Appia imo Publicii Clivo ad Portam Trigeminam, qui locus Salinae appellantur,

as Frontinus (I. 5) says. The masonry delivery tank or reservoir stood here and the water was distributed from it in lead pipes. During the reign of Augustus, an additional supply of water was obtained for this aqueduct by a branch entirely underground, called the Aqua Appia Augusta, about six miles long, which connected with the Aqua Appia near its entrance into the city.

Anio Vetus. The second of the ancient aqueducts was constructed between the years 272 and 270 B.C., constructed by means of the proceeds from the booty taken from Pyrrhus. Its supply was taken from the river Anio, above Tivoli, about twenty miles from Rome. The total length of the aqueduct was about forty-one miles, the increase in length being due to its development of the intersecting valleys of the tributary streams. Of its total length, only a little over 1,000 feet, just outside the city near the Porta Praenestina, are above ground. The upper part of this aqueduct, from its source to

Gallicano, has been traced, some remains have been found within the city and described by Lanciani, but its route across the Campagna has not been found. Where the aqueduct is above ground, the *specus* or conduit was constructed to the Servian Wall, following the line mortar, and coated with cement on the inside.

This aqueduct, like the Aqua Appia, entered the city near the temple of *Spes Vetus*, a little to the right of the Porta Maggiore. It was constructed to the Servian Wall, following the line of that wall to the Porta Esquilina (or the " arch of Gallienus "). A branch of this aqueduct was constructed by Augustus; the branch, beginning at the second milestone outside the city, led to the south and gave the aqueduct another delivery point within the city, near the Porta Metrovia.

The gradient of the Anio Vetus varied considerably; as given by Lanciani, the mean fall from the intake to Tivoli is 1.937 in 1000; from Tivoli to Gallicano, 0.933 in 1000; and from Gallicano to the city, 4.125 in 1000; but there are no data as to the intermediate variations.

These two aqueducts entered Rome at too low an altitude to supply the higher parts of the city; the Aqua Appia led across the Aventine to the base of that hill and the Anio Vetus to the Esquiline; the delivery point of Appia was but sixty-six feet above sea level, and of Anio Vetus one hundred and fifty-seven feet. The higher hills of Rome all have an altitude over one hundred and fifty feet, which is the approximate height of the two lowest, the Aventine and the Capitoline.

Aqua Marcia. About one hundred and twenty-seven years after the construction of Anio Vetus, Frontinus (I. 7) tells us that the water supply had become greatly diminished by leakage, and an additional supply was needed for the increased population of the city. The Praetor, Quintus Marcius Rex, was commissioned by the Senate to repair the old aqueducts and to investigate the practicability of obtaining an additional supply. Acting under this commission, Marcius built the third aqueduct, the Aqua Marcia, between the years 144 and 140 B.C., i.e. very soon after the close of the third Carthaginian war. The Marcia was a high-level aqueduct, delivering its waters to the distributing station on the Viminal Hill at an elevation of one hundred and ninety-two feet; from this point the water was carried in pipes to the Capitoline and Caelian hills and to other parts of the city.

Its sources were springs in the valley of the Anio, near the thirty-sixth milestone on the Via Valeria. Its course turned the Anio as far as Tivoli, where it turns to the south, tunneling through the hills and crossing the intervening valleys on masonry bridges. The course of this aqueduct has been traced from its sources to Gallicano and that part of the course is very similar to the lines followed by the Anio Vetus and the later Aqua Claudia and Anio Novus. This work up among the mountains still remains in part and still inspires our wonder. The total length of the aqueduct was about 59 miles, far the greater part of which was under ground; at the sixth milestone from the city on the Via Latina, it emerged above ground and was carried on triumphal arches to the Porta Praenestina.

The later aqueducts, Tepula and Julia, were carried across the Campagna on these arches of Marcia.

At the Porta Praenestina, the arches continued northward to the point where, later, the Porta Tiburtina (or " S. Lorenzo ") stood. This line of arches was incorporated in the wall of Aurelian, as is well known, carrying the waters of Marcia and, above, those of Tepula and Julia.

Agrippa restored this aqueduct, as did Augustus, who added another spring higher up, the channel from the new spring being connected with both Marcia and the later Aqua Claudia, so that the water could be turned into either aqueduct as might be required, the additional supply being kept in reserve for seasons of protracted dry weather (*Mon. Ancyr.*, IV. 11, Front., I. 12).

The waters of the Aqua Marcia were the best in ancient Rome. Martial (VI. 42. 18) praises the pure cold waters of the Virgo and of Marcia, and Statius (*Silv.*, I. 5. 26) says:

Virgo iuvat Marsasque nives et frigora ducens
Marcia,

Marcia bringing Marsian snows and cold,

while Pliny enthusiastically praises the superiority of the Marcian waters (*N.H.*, XXXI. 3. 24. 41): Clarissima aquarum omnium in toto orbe frigoris salubritatisque palma praeconio urbis Marcia est.

In Nero's reign an underground branch was built leading from the Porta Tiburtina to the Porta Capena; this was extended by Trajan to the Aventine; Caracalla added another branch, called the Aqua Antoniniana, which led to his baths, crossing the Appian Way on the "Arch of Drusus"; Diocletian restored the aqueduct, as had Marcus Aurelius before (*C. I. L.*, VI. 1245).

The waters of Marcia now furnish the supply of the modern aqueduct, the "Acqua Marcia-Pia," completed in 1870; the construction of this aqueduct was almost the last act of the Papal government, its completion being celebrated by Pope Pius IX but a few days before the Italian army entered Rome.

The aqueduct was carried over the Porta Capena, as has been said, and evidently was not always in repair.

Capena grandi porta qua pluit gutta (Martial, III. 47. 1)

It was through this gate that Bassus passed as he was leaving the city and the dripping aqueduct that passed over the gate added to his annoyance, the

madidamque Capenam, of Juvenal (III. 11).

Shakespeare follows Plutarch closely, when he makes Brutus say in *Coriolanus* (Act II, Sc. 3):

*T*he *noble house of the Marcians, from whence
came
T*hat Ancus Marcius, Numa's daughter's son,
W*ho after great Hostilius was King;
O*f the same house Publius and Quintus were,
T*hat our best waters brought in conduits hither.*

Aqua Tepula. This aqueduct was built in
125 B.C.; its sources lie in volcanic springs on
the Alban Hills, between Frascati and Rocca di
Papa, about two miles west of the tenth milestone from Rome on the Via Latina. As originally constructed it was brought into Rome in
its own channel, although we do not know its
original course; but in 33 B.C., after Tepula had
been in service for ninety-two years, Agrippa,
who had been appointed *Curator Aquarum* and
who was then building the Julia, turned the
water of Julia into the channel of the Tepula,
and the two waters, uniting at the tenth milestone of the Via Latina, flowed in the same
channel for about four miles. About six miles
from Rome, they were again divided into two
channels, and thence continued, each in its own
channel, carried on the arches of the Aqua Marcia, to the city. The purpose of mingling the
two streams was to reduce the temperature of
Tepula, which was derived from warm springs

with a temperature of 63 degrees Fahrenheit; combined in the proportion of one of Tepula to three of Julia, the resulting temperature was about 53 or 54 degrees. The *specus* or conduit of Tepula was built of concrete, while that of Marcia was built of large dimension stone. Mr. Herschel suggests that this was for greater convenience of construction on the top of the already existing masonry of Marcia. A similar construction was afterwards adopted in the aqueduct Anio Novus, which was built on the top of the dimension stone *specus* of the Claudian aqueduct.

Aqua Julia. This aqueduct was built by Agrippa, 33 B.C. Its water comes from cold springs in the Alban Hills, about two miles west of the twelfth milestone on the Via Latina, a mile or two beyond the springs of Tepula. The point where the two aqueducts, Tepula and Julia, divide, being near the place where Marcia's long arcade began, both aqueducts cross the Campagna on the arches of Marcia, Tepula on top of Marcia, and Julia on top of Tepula. They are carried thus to the Porta Praenestina and thence to the Porta Tiburtina. The waters of the Julia aqueduct were carried to the Esquiline Hill, where the remains of a *cas-*

tellum (of later date) are still to be seen in the piazza Vittorio Emanuele. The total length of the Aqua Tepula was about twelve miles and that of the Julia, about fourteen miles.

Aqua Virgo. This aqueduct was built by Agrippa in 19 B.C. Its supply was taken from springs in the valley of the Anio, near the ancient eighth milestone on the Via Collatina, not far from the source of Appia, near Salone.

Virgo appellata est, quod quaerentibus aquam militibus puella virguncula venas quasdam monstravit, quas secuti qui foderant, ingentem aquae modum invenerunt,

Frontinus (I. 10) says, and he adds that a small temple, situated near the spring, contained a painting illustrating this origin of the aqueduct. Cassiodorus, however, gives a different theory: " Virgo's stream is so pure that the name, according to common opinion, is derived from the fact that those waters are never sullied."

The water of the Aqua Virgo was remarkably clear, but was delivered at Rome at too low an elevation to be available for the general supply; it was constructed primarily for the baths of Agrippa in the Campus Martius, serving, also, the later baths of Alexander Severus. Just outside of the city, near the Porta Praenestina, the Virgo turned to the north and entered the city on the Pincian Hill, east of the Piazza di Spagna. The Aqua Virgo was the subject of frequent restorations, notably by Claudius in A.D. 52, and by Popes Nicholas V in 1453, and Pius V in 1570. It is still in service and is now known by the name of " Acqua Vergine "; it supplies water for the Trevi fountain, those in the Piazza di Spagna, etc. During the long period between the destruction of the major aqueducts and the completion of the Aqua Felice in 1585, the Virgo was the only outside source of supply, and when it was out of service the city of Rome depended entirely on the Tiber and wells and springs within the city, thus returning to the status that existed before the building of the first aqueduct:

Ab urbe condita per annos CCCCXLI (312/$_3$ *B.C.*) contenti fuerunt Romani usu aquarum, quas aut ex Tiberi aut ex puteis aut ex fontibus hauriebant. (Front., *De. Aq.*, I § 4.)

The total length of Virgo was a little over thirteen miles, of which over twelve were underground. A short stretch, within the city, was carried on arches.

Aqua Alsietina. This aqueduct, also called Aqua Augusta, was built by Augustus, about A.D. 10, to supply water for an artificial lake, called the Naumachia, which he had made for the purpose of giving nautical exhibitions and naval sham battles. The exact site of this Naumachia, in the Transtibertine district, is not known, but it was probably a short distance north of the Villa Corsini. Even in the time of Alexander Severus only slight traces of the Naumachia remained. In the *Monumentum Ancyranum* (ch. xxiii, IV. 43) we read that ground was excavated for 1800 feet in length and 1200 in width, and that thirty beaked triremes and quadriremes were engaged in the initial combat. The water of the Alsietina was unfit for drinking and besides supplying water for the Naumachia it was later used for watering gardens. It had no public delivery. Its source was the Lacus Alsietinus, the modern lake Martignano, located some twenty-one miles north of Rome, in southern Etruria, between Veii and the ancient Lacus Sabatinus. The exact route of the aqueduct has not been determined, though some portions of the ancient structure have recently been located near the American Academy.

[79]

Aqua Claudia. This aqueduct was begun
A.D. 38, during the reign of Caligula, and completed by Claudius in the year A.D. 52.

TI · CLAVDIVS. . . .
AQUAS · CLAVDIAM · EX · FONTIBVS. . .
ITEM · ANIENEM · NOVAM. . . . SVA · IMPENSA ·
IN · VRBEM · PERDVCENDAS · CVRAVIT.

(*C. I. L.*, VI. 1256).

Tiberius Claudius caused the waters of Claudia
and of Anio Novus to be brought to the city
at his own expense.

This is the aqueduct whose arches remain the
most imposing in the Roman Campagna. It
received its supply from springs in the valley
of the Anio, not far from the springs of Marcia,
and was said to be next to Marcia in excellence
(Front., I. 13). It followed the same general
course as Marcia and the other aqueducts that
have their source in the same region, toward
Gallicano, but about thirty-six years after it
was built, Domitian shortened its line by the
construction of a tunnel over three miles long
through Monte Affliano. Except for the valley
crossings, the conduit of Claudia was entirely
underground, from its source to the point where
it emerged from the hillside, a little less than

[80]

seven miles from Rome. Its total length was something less than forty-four miles, of which about thirty-four were underground. From the point of its emergence from the hillside it was carried about three thousand feet on a low masonry substructure, and thence for a trifle over six miles on a long line of magnificent arches.

The arches of Claudia vary somewhat in the length of their span, being generally eighteen or twenty feet in the clear; the arch rings are about three feet deep at the crown. The tops of the arch stones form the bottom of the water channel. The water channel, or *specus,* is built up of four courses of dimension stone, each course being about eighteen inches in thickness. The general height of the masonry is between ninety and one hundred feet. The piers are about eight feet thick, very large for the length of the span; they are heavy enough to serve as abutment piers, as, in fact, many of them have been serving for centuries where the adjoining arches have been removed; it is to this excess of strength that those that remain owe their preservation.

During the reign of Nero, a branch was built from the Claudia, near its point of entrance into the city, south of the Porta Praenestina, to the Caelian Hill, which was carried on a line of arches nearly a mile and a half long. These arches were called *Arcus Caelemontani,* or *Arcus Neroniani,* and their brickwork, as later restored, is of the finest in the ancient city. This branch was extended by Domitian to the Palatine by an inverted siphon, made of lead pipe, twelve inches in diameter, under a head of one hundred and forty feet. After this inverted siphon had been in service considerably over one hundred years, the Emperor Septimius Severus had it replaced by an aqueduct bridge of masonry, consisting of four tiers of arches, superimposed one above the other, like the arches of the Pont du Gard, the total length of this structure being about fourteen hundred feet and its height about one hundred and forty.

The reason for replacing the inverted siphon by a high-level aqueduct bridge is not known to us. Those who attribute the construction of the arches of Marcia and Claudia to the fondness of the Romans for display may here find support for their opinion, but there is to be considered the possibility that the old leaden pipes under the pressure of so great a head may have shown weakness in their soldered joints and seams and had been giving trouble. The danger of rupture of a pipe in the city under so great pressure may have been one of the reasons for the change.

The Aqua Claudia, curiously, had to be repaired early in its history, by Vespasian, and then by Titus. The aqueduct approached the city, as did so many others, at a point near the Porta Praenestina. A stretch of about 1025 feet of arches, leading south from the Porta Praenestina, was incorporated in the later Aurelian Wall.

Anio Novus.

Vicit antecedentes aquarum ductus novissimum impendium operis incohati a Gaio Caesare et peracti a Claudio (Pliny, *N.H.*, XXXVI. 15. 24. 122).

The most recent cost of the work begun by Gaius Caesar and finished by Claudius surpassed that of all previous aqueducts.

The new Anio was built at the same time as Claudia, but takes its water from the river, at Subiaco, above the source of Claudia and at a higher elevation, near the forty-second milestone on the Via Sublacensis; its course is parallel to that of Claudia from its source to the point where both emerge from the ground before crossing the Campagna. Its total length is about 56 miles, of which about 47 miles are underground; it was, thus, one of the longest of the aqueducts. For nearly seven miles it was carried on the arches of Claudia; the *specus* of the Anio Novus (built of brick and concrete) was above that of the Claudian *specus* (built of dimension stone). As the water of the Anio was very muddy and unfit for use after heavy rains, a large settling basin or *piscina limaria* was constructed between the river and the head of the aqueduct; four miles below, the waters of a stream, the *rivus Herculaneus,* were admitted into the *specus,* to purify the water supply; during the reign of Trajan, the quality of the water was further improved; the intake was moved farther up stream and water taken from one of the artificial lakes, near Subiaco, that Nero had constructed by building a dam across the river, for the improvement of the estate about his country villa. One castellum received the waters of the Claudian aqueduct and of the Aqua Anio Novus; it was situated near the Porta Praenestina, and in it the waters of the two aqueducts were mixed.

Four aqueducts, Anio Vetus, Marcia, Clau-

dia, and Anio Novus, cross the valley of the
Acqua rossa on the same bridge, the Ponte
Lupo. Originally built for the Anio Vetus, the
Ponte Lupo was widened and raised in height
as each new aqueduct was built; as at first constructed, it was about two hundred and sixty-
six feet long, about thirty-six feet high and
about nine feet wide; the completed structure,
carrying the four aqueducts, was about five
hundred and eight feet long, about one hundred and five feet high, and about forty-six feet
wide; on the top of Anio Vetus and alongside
the higher walls of Marcia was a wagon road,
and on the top of Anio Novus a bridle path.
The Ponte Lupo contains, in one structure, examples of Roman masonry construction covering a period of three hundred years. This is
one of the most interesting points in the Tibur-
Anio region, where so many aqueducts had their
beginnings. It is situated near Gallicano.

Frontinus' admiration for the system of aqueducts, as completed in his day, was deservedly
great:

Tot aquarum tam multis necessariis molibus
pyramidas videlicet otiosas compares aut cetera
inertia sed fama celebritata opera Graecorum
(I. 16).

"With such an array of indispensable structures carrying so many waters, compare, if you will, the idle Pyramids or the useless, though famous, works of the Greeks!" (Trans. of C. E. Bennett, in *The Loeb Classical Library*.)

Aqua Trajana. This aqueduct was constructed by Trajan, A.D. 109, a few years after the death of Frontinus, in order to furnish a better water supply for the region "across the Tiber." It was supplied by springs which were near the Lacus Sabatinus, or Lago Bracciano as it is called today, in southern Etruria, and it followed nearly the same course as the Alsietina. It was about 37 miles in length, entirely underground, and delivered its water into a castellum on the Janiculum Hill. This aqueduct had the highest delivery point of all the aqueducts. The quantity of water and the available head were sufficient to furnish power for a number of flour mills, during the later empire, on the slope of the Janiculum.

The aqueduct was cut by the Goths during the siege of Rome in A.D. 537, and the mills were put out of service. Belisarius, who commanded the Roman army in defence of the city, moored two barges in the river just below the Pons Aurelius, where the water of the Tiber came rushing out between the piers of the bridge, and securing the boats together at a proper distance apart, set up a water wheel between them, which furnished sufficient power to run two mills on each boat; other boats were added in pairs below the first two; and, if Procopius may be relied upon, enough grain was ground in this way to supply the city with flour. (Proc., *De Bello Goth.*, V. xix. 19.)

Trajan's aqueduct was restored by Pope Paul V, in 1611, and the aqueduct still bears the name of Acqua Paola.

Aqua Alexandrina. This, the last of the ancient aqueducts, was constructed by Alexander Severus, A.D. 226, to supply his baths in the Campus Martius. It was supplied by springs about thirteen miles from Rome, near Gabii and Lake Regillus. The aqueduct was about fourteen miles long, a little over six miles of which were above ground. These ancient springs now form a part of the supply of the modern aqueduct, the Acqua Felice, constructed in 1585 by Pope Sixtus V.

Thus we have seen that eleven great aqueducts brought water into Rome, carrying the water supply for distances varying from ten to fifty-nine miles. The great majority of these aqueducts brought water from springs of the Anio, but two, the Tepula and the Julia, had their sources in the Alban hills, and two others, the Alsietina and the Trajana, in southern Etruria. The Porta Praenestina marked the point of arrival of most of these aqueducts, eight in number: Appia, Anio Vetus, Marcia, Tepula, Julia, Virgo, Claudia, Anio Novus; perhaps the Aqua Alexandrina also arrived near by. Two, the Alsietina and the Trajana, carried waters to the Janiculan side of the city, and of the former only slightest traces remain. Branches from the main aqueducts supplied every part of the city. *Castella* served as reservoirs, and pipes of lead, clay, and metal were all known to the Romans.

The most celebrated of the aqueducts of the provinces was that known by the modern name of Pont du Gard, which carries the Aqueduct of Nîmes over the valley of the Gardon, and which has been called the most beautiful aqueduct bridge in the world. It was fittingly built at Nîmes, the ancient Nemausus, one of the chief cities of southern Gaul, the most advanced in culture and the most intensely Roman of all the western provinces. It has been supposed to have been the work of Agrippa, on the occasion of his visit to Gaul in 19 B.C., but Friedlaender states that an inscription found on the spot attributes it to Veranius.

It consists of three tiers of arches, the piers of the second tier resting directly over those of the lowest tier. The arches of the two lower tiers are of three lengths of span, 51, 63, and 80½ feet, in marked contrast to the shorter spans of the aqueducts of Rome; the smaller arches of the topmost tier have spans of the uniform length of eleven feet, nine inches.

The total length of the structure is nearly nine hundred feet and its total height is one hundred and sixty feet. The width is twenty feet, nine inches at the lowest tier of arches, fifteen feet at the intermediate tier, and ten feet at the uppermost tier. The keystone of the longest arch is five feet, three inches in depth, the other keystones of the lowest tier, five feet. A peculiarity of its construction is that the arches of the lowest tier are built in four parallel rings, and the arches of the intermediate tier in three rings, while the arches of the top tier are continuous from face to face. These parallel rings of the lower tiers are not bonded or tied together in any way, and there is no mortar or any cementing material in any of the arch rings, but cement mortar was used in the concrete which formed the *specus* or conduit through which the water flowed. This method of building the arches in parallel rings appears to have been adopted for the purpose of economizing in the centering.

The aqueduct was cut at the ends of the bridge when Nemausus was besieged by the Goths and Vandals in the fifth century, but no injury was done to the main structure. Repairs were made in 1743, at which time the piers were lengthened to make a roadway. The length of the aqueduct is about thirty miles, with a uniform gradient of 0.04 per hundred.

The city of Lugdunum, now Lyons, had four aqueducts; the most important, that of Mt. Pilate, built by Claudius about A.D. 50, had several aqueduct bridges; it is most notable, however, for having three sets of inverted siphons. The first, crossing the valley of the Garon, would have required, according to Leger, an aqueduct bridge about two hundred and fifteen feet high with four or five tiers of arches, the highest tier nearly fifteen hundred feet long. The inverted siphon was composed of nine lines of lead pipe, eight and five-eighths inches in diameter and one and six-tenths inches in thickness of metal; the descending and ascending branches were carried on masonry on a slope of about forty-five degrees; at the middle of the slope the number of the pipes was increased to eighteen and the size reduced to $6\frac{5}{8}$ inches to resist the increased pressure; the level portion of the siphon, or, as Vitruvius termed it, the *venter*, was carried across the valley on a masonry bridge of thirty arches about fifty feet high.

The second siphon on the same aqueduct, crossing the valley of Bonant, would have required a bridge three hundred feet high; the construction was similar to the siphons of the Garon, the *venter* being carried on a masonry bridge over sixty feet in height, under a head of two hundred and forty feet. The third siphon on the Mt. Pilate aqueduct and another on the aqueduct of Mt. d'Or were treated in the same way. The designs of these aqueducts appear to have been made with the intention of saving in the masonry and at the same time avoiding too great pressure on the lead pipes of the siphon. Leger expresses the opinion that the height of the masonry at the crossing of the Garon might have been considerably reduced without risk, but considers the problem very skilfully worked out, with the limited resources of the time.[5]

The purpose of carrying the siphons on masonry appears to have been to reduce the pressure on the pipes. In other cases the Romans buried their pipes, and on a branch of the aqueduct of Arles, an inverted siphon crossed the river Rhone with the pipes laid in the bed of the river; some of these pipes have been recovered.

Among many other examples of inverted siphons, the most remarkable were those of Alatri, constructed about 150 B.C., by a wealthy and public-spirited citizen, Betilianus Varo, which are said to have sustained a head of three hundred and forty feet.

Of the other aqueducts of Italy, that of Spoleto is almost the only one surviving. Traces of aqueducts are found at Pompeii, Aquileia, Paestum, and other cities. The aqueduct of Rimini is said to have been of particular magnificence.

The aqueduct of Spoleto is still in use. The time of its construction is variously estimated from the period of the later empire to the time of Theodoric in the early sixth century, and even as late as the seventh or eighth century. It is remarkable for its pointed arches and the lightness and height of its piers. It is built in two tiers of arches: the ten arches of the lower tier have spans of about seventy-three feet, at a height of over three hundred and sixty feet above the river; the thirty pointed arches in the upper tier have a span of six metres with a rise of four metres; the total height of the bridge is four hundred and thirty feet and its total length is eight hundred and thirty feet.

The aqueduct of Metz crossed the Moselle on an arched bridge thirty-six hundred feet in length and over a hundred feet high. Seven of its arches and ten piers remain; the clear span was about seventeen and one-half feet.

The aqueduct of Fréjus, the ancient Forum Julii, was about twenty-five miles long; on its line were a number of arched bridges; in some of them the piers are strongly counterforted.

The city of Lutetia, now Paris, had three aqueducts; the most important was that of Arcueil, built by the Emperor Julian about A.D. 360. This aqueduct crossed the valley of the Bièvre, near Arcueil, on a bridge of six arches of about twenty-six feet span. It was destroyed by the Normans in the ninth century, and its remains were not discovered until 1544. Between the years 1613 and 1624 a new aqueduct was built to supply water for the gardens of Luxembourg. In Leger's opinion the old aqueduct was better than the new, especially in its gradients, which were much more regular. The old name of the ancient village, Arcus Julianus, still lingers in the modern name of Arcueil.

More than thirty cities of ancient Gaul were provided with aqueducts: Marseilles had three; Aix, four; Vienne, three; and Antibes, two, one of which is still in service.

In Spain the great aqueduct bridge of Segovia, built under Trajan, A.D. 109, is renowned for its grandeur and its excellent preservation. The aqueduct is nine to ten miles long. For the greater part of its length it is a surface channel, then for about half a mile it is carried on a low masonry support, and finally crosses the valley at Segovia on a magnificent arched bridge about twenty-six hundred feet in length, and over ninety feet high. The piers are built of heavy granite blocks, rough faced, with precisely dressed joints, and laid without cement. There are two tiers of arches of about sixteen and one-half feet span. The piers are but six feet wide and about eight feet long. The arches of the lower tier are about fifty-nine feet high and those of the upper tier thirty-four, making a total height of ninety-three feet above the ground at the lowest part of the valley.

At Tarragona is a magnificent aqueduct bridge, partially preserved, of two tiers of arches. The total length was about seven hundred feet and the greatest height about ninety feet.

Merida had two aqueducts. On each of them were several arched bridges. One of them had three tiers of arches, of which there still remain ten arches and thirty piers. The piers were built of stone and brick in alternating courses.

The aqueduct of Toledo had a bridge of two tiers of arches, one hundred feet high.

The aqueducts discharged the water into distributing reservoirs, or *castella;* these were usually ornamented with statues, and had fountains flowing continuously into marble basins. From the *castella,* distributing mains were laid to the points of local delivery, where the people came with their water jars to obtain the household supply; they were also connected by service pipes with public buildings and many dwelling houses. For private service a specified rate was charged, depending upon the size of the ferrule, *calix*, or *modulus*, that connected the service pipe with the street main. As might be expected, some of the consumers had larger connections with the mains than were specified in their water leases, and there were others taking water who had no leases at all. Frontinus recounts the troubles he had with these illegal consumers and says that the extent of their fraudulent practices might be estimated by the great quantity of lead pipe that he had confiscated.

The pipes in the distribution system were generally of lead, but earthenware pipes were often used for moderate pressures, and were preferred as less likely to contaminate the water; earthenware pipes were often strengthened by embedding them in concrete, and elbows were usually made of stone. The lead pipes were made of sheet lead, cast in sheets ten feet long, and cut to the proper width to make pipe of the desired diameter. The edges, usually flanged, were brought together and soldered with lead; this method of making pipe continued to be used until the Middle Ages. The fittings, stop cocks, and faucets were of bronze. The faucets were frequently of ornamental designs, such as the heads of animals.

The quantity of water brought to Rome by the aqueducts has been the subject of much discussion, and its determination is now practically impossible from the want of sufficiently reliable data; it is certain, however, that the quantity has been greatly exaggerated by the earlier archaeologists. The unit used by Frontinus in gauging the aqueducts was the *quinaria,* which he took to be the quantity of water discharged through a pipe of five-fourths of one digit in diameter, known by the name of *fistula quinaria;* the next larger size, the *fistula senaria* being six-fourths of one digit in diameter, and so on; the digit being one sixteenth of a Roman foot, or o.728 inch. In making his calculations Frontinus assumed that the discharge of an aqueduct was equal to the total discharge of a large number of small pipes whose combined cross-sectional areas were equal to the cross-sectional area of the aqueduct, which is far from correct; and he also failed to take into account the effect of the velocity of the flowing stream on the rate of discharge; consequently, although he went to a great deal of painstaking trouble, his calculations are of little value in determining the actual quantity of water carried; they afford, however, a very interesting illustration of the difficulties of Roman arithmetic. (Front., I. 37 *seq.*)

Frontinus, however, was not unacquainted with some of the principles of hydraulics. He knew that the rate of flow was greater when the water came from a high point and when it flowed through a short pipe than when it came from a lower point or flowed through a longer pipe, but not being able to assign definite values to these factors, he was unable to take them into account in his calculations.

The water leases, that specified the size of the ferrule, also provided that it should not be less than twelve digits or nine Roman inches long and that the pipe leading from it should be of the same diameter as the ferrule for not less than fifty feet. From this it has been inferred that the Romans understood the principle of the *vena contracta* and the Venturi tube. It is not likely that this was the case; in Bk. II, ch. 112, Frontinus explains that in some instances where the ferrules were of the size specified in the leases, pipes of a larger size had been attached to them, whence, he says, " the water not being forced for the lawful distance but being passed through short restrictions easily filled the larger pipe." In this passage the term " short restrictions " is contrasted with the words " lawful distance," and Frontinus seems merely to indicate the opinion that the flow of water would be greater with a short length of smaller pipe than it would be if the entire distance of fifty feet were of smaller pipe; and therefore to protect the department the use of a pipe larger than the *calix* was prohibited. These is nothing in Frontinus to indicate that the Romans had any idea of an ajutage of varying diameter or with a flaring outlet.[6]

Lanciani says that only two of these ferrules have been found; they were both about 8¾, or nine Roman inches long, and of uniform diameter from end to end; Herschel doubts whether those mentioned by Lanciani were really *calices,* and refers to two at Naples which, he says, were about nine inches long and one digit in internal diameter.

When the new aqueduct Marcia-Pia was under construction a survey was made of the old Marcia near the intake. In all of the old aqueducts the line of the water surface is plainly marked on the sides of the conduit by deposits of carbonate of lime, and from these marks the hydraulic gradient of the running water was found to have been 0.06 per hundred, or three feet and two inches per mile; from this and the cross-sectional area of the stream, the rate of flow has been calculated to have been thirty-five million gallons per day, which is not more than half of the estimates usually given. Making allowance for leakage, Mr. Herschel concludes that a probable estimate of the quantity of water actually delivered at Rome by all the aqueducts was about eighty-four million gallons per day, and making further allowance for the frequency with which some of the aqueducts were out of service and for the systematic diversion of water, the quantity available at Rome was probably very much less.

In order to prevent the obstruction of the smaller pipes of the distribution system by pebbles carried along by the rapid current, catch basins, called *piscinae,* were interposed on the line of the aqueducts. Their purpose was at first obscure, but it was clearly indicated when a large mound near one of them was opened and found to be entirely composed of pebbles thrown out of the *piscina* at its periodical cleanings.

The principal sources of the Roman aqueducts were in the great limestone beds of travertine, and the water was exceedingly hard. The sides of the conduits are coated with thick deposits of carbonate of lime, and as the conduits leaked profusely the ruins are covered with incrustations, in many cases of enormous size. Herschel compares the incrustations under the arches of Claudia to the trunks of huge vines, some of them being nine inches thick, and showing, when broken, a series of concentric rings like the growth rings on trees.

The excessive leakage of the aqueducts is no doubt the explanation of the frequent repairs and restorations of the aqueducts related by the historians and recorded on inscriptions. Frontinus states that Marcius restored the Appia and Anio Vetus, and Agrippa, when building Julia, restored the Appia, Anio and Marcia. The Virgo was repaired in 31, 43, and 44; Claudia in 71, after ten years of service and nine years of disuse, and was again repaired in 80 and 84.

Some archaeologists have expressed the opinion that these frequent restorations were indicative of very defective construction, but it is inconceivable that the builders of the piers and arches that have stood so many centuries could have built parts of the same structure so badly as to require such frequent rebuilding. The only reasonable explanation of the " restorations " is that they were made on account of the leakage of the conduits and not because of any structural deficiency of the masonry. A few years' exposure to the expansion and contraction of alternating day and night, and of winter and summer, especially in the case of a high-level aqueduct on a line six miles long, is quite sufficient to account for the leakage of the conduits.

The arches of the Claudia on the Campagna that still remain standing afford several examples of the attempts that were made to stop the leaks, usually by building an auxiliary arc of several rings of brick work beneath the soffit of the leaking arch, and filling the space between with concrete tightly rammed. A similar construction is frequently adopted to support a broken or yielding arch, and some of the archaeological writers have assumed that such was the purpose here. In this opinion Choisy concurs, but the arches thus reinforced do not appear to have yielded, and are themselves many times stronger than the auxiliary arches supposedly built to sustain them. In at least one case, the supports of the subsidiary arch have been taken away, leaving the brick arch and the concrete filling hanging from the arch above. It is much more reasonable to conclude with Herschel, that these brick arches were not intended for support and could only have been intended to overcome the leakage.

It is not greatly to the discredit of the Roman engineers that they were unable to maintain a permanently watertight channel in their masonry aqueducts; similar failures have occurred in quite recent times. Mr. Herschel gives an instance of a masonry aqueduct built in 1874, where special attention was given in the design to provide against the effects of expansion and contraction without success; when another aqueduct was constructed by the same engineers in 1898, they overcame the difficulty by lining the conduit with sheet lead, which is precisely the method recommended by Frontinus for repairing an aqueduct that had failed.[7]

Great wonder has been often expressed that the Romans built their long high-level aqueducts of masonry, when it would apparently have been so much easier to put them underground. The Romans have been accused of ignorance of the hydraulic principle of the siphon, notwithstanding the fact that Pliny clearly enunciated it in his *Natural History* and Vitruvius described siphons and outlined the conditions that indicated their use. Siphons on a large scale were in actual use in some of the more important aqueducts; the siphons of Lugdunum were constructed about the same time as the Claudia was building, and the siphons of Alatri were constructed before the Marcia. Duruy, in his *History of Rome,* ascribes the building of the high aqueducts to the fondness of the Romans for display, saying that " rather than hide their aqueducts underground they caused them to traverse the Roman Campagna upon majestic arches," and even Leger declares that they were constructed " in great part to satisfy their amour-propre," and "without great necessity." Beyond question, the Romans were fond of display, and doubtless their " amour-propre " found full satisfaction in those " majestic arches," but their construction was based on sound engineering principles; and when Frontinus in his enthusiasm interrupts the quiet course of his description of the aqueducts, to contrast their massive masonry with the " idle pyramids," the word he uses is " necessary." It was the adaptation of means to end, and the accomplishment of a useful and necessary, and at the same time difficult enterprise, that most awakened Roman pride. The pride that they took in their aqueducts was in the completion of a great project and not mere vainglory and " amour-propre."

It is a difficult undertaking to maintain a masonry conduit under heavy outward pressure, and the Romans had not the facilities for making lead pipe of the large size required, and of sufficient strength and reliability, nor even in sufficient quantity, for so long a line, and their only recourse was to build a high-level aqueduct on approximately the hydraulic grade line. A parallel instance of the construction of a high-level bridge in preference to an inverted siphon may be cited in the case of a quite modern aqueduct. When the first Croton aqueduct was built, about the year 1840, the line of the aqueduct was located to conform closely to the contour of the ground, until reaching the Harlem River, which it crossed on a bridge of fifteen full-centered arches at an elevation of over one hundred feet above high water in the river, although in the same aqueduct inverted siphons were used in crossing the neighboring Manhattan Valley, under a pressure head of nearly one hundred feet. The second Croton aqueduct, constructed about forty years later, follows a more direct course and crosses the Harlem River by an inverted siphon through a tunnel, cut in the solid rock, ten feet, six inches in diameter, thirteen hundred feet long, and three hundred and seven feet below the water. In other words, the Marcian and Claudian aqueducts were carried on high arches, like the first Croton, because that was the best form of construction under the circumstances, with the available material.

The second Croton and the new Marcia-Pia followed the modern practice, the principal reason being the availability of heavy cast iron pipe and, in the case of the Croton, improved methods of tunneling.

Since the ruins of the aqueducts even today show the excellence of their construction, the question naturally arises, what has caused their destruction? In general, this has been due, not so much to the decay of time, or to military demolition, as to the tearing down of the old masonry to obtain material for other structures. Lanciani thinks it probable that the arches of both the Marcia and the Claudia were practically intact up to the time when Pope Sixtus V began the construction of the Acqua Felice, when the builders of the new aqueduct were permitted to take the stone of the old Marcia, long out of service. Many of Claudia's arches and piers were taken from time to time for use elsewhere, some of them being sold to the highest bidder at public sale.[8]

VI. THE ROADS

AS THE ruined aqueducts may be considered memorials of Rome's departed grandeur, the roads may with equal propriety be taken as symbols of the unity of the ancient empires; if less impressive than the aqueducts as monuments of Roman civilization, they hold a more important place as the instruments of the diffusion of that civilization throughout the empire, and even as the chief material factors in the extension and maintenance of the empire itself; as Smiles says in his life of Telford: " It was the roads as well as the legion that made the Romans masters of the world," — the construction of the great system of Roman highways having effected a revolution, which has been compared to that effected in the modern world by the construction of the railways; a revolution like that caused by the roads built by Telford in the Scottish highlands, where the improvement in the condition of the people has been described as " unequalled in the history of any peoples."

The Romans began the construction of paved roads in Italy, soon after the extension of their dominion over Latium; the first being the Appian Way, through Latium, from Rome to Capua; this was followed by others until Italy was covered by a network of main roads and branches, while from the northern boundaries of Italy, the roads were extended to every part of the empire.[9]

Leger (*Trav. Pub.*, p. 247), following Bergier, gives the total length of three hundred and seventy-two highways, listed in the Itineraries of Antoninus, as 53,568 Roman miles, or in round numbers about 50,000 English miles; besides which there were many roads of secondary importance and branch roads not included in the Itineraries.

The Romans varied the construction of their roads according to their importance, using generally the material found in the vicinity; where suitable material was not available, they did not hesitate to bring it from a distance. They paid special attention to the preparation of the subgrade, removing the surface earth until firm ground was found, which they consolidated by ramming; on soft ground they occasionally drove piles.

The typical road bed, as described by Leger and other authorities, was then built up, substantially as follows: on a bed of sand from four to six inches in thickness, or on mortar about an inch thick, which was called the *pavimentum*, were laid four layers of masonry.[10] The first layer, called the *statumen*, consisted of flat or squared stones laid in cement or bound by clay; the *statumen* was usually about one foot thick, or on bad ground two feet; on rock foundation the *statumen* was omitted. The second layer, called *rudus* or *ruderatio*, was a bed of concrete, made with smaller stones or pebbles, gravel, or crushed hard brick or tiles, rammed hard, about ten inches thick after ramming; in default of cement, clay was used instead. The third layer, or *nucleus*, was composed of a concrete of gravel, or coarse sand, finer than the preceding, a foot to a foot and a half thick, put down in successive layers and rolled. The fourth or top layer, called *summum dorsum*, *summa crusta*, was varied according to the locality; it was usually from eight to twelve inches thick. The completed road was called *via strata* or *munita;* the total thickness varied from three and a half to four feet.[11]

On the great roads of Italy the *summa crusta* was ordinarily of silex, or lava, shaped in irregular hexagons or polygons from one to three feet in diameter; the upper surface dressed smooth, the bed left rough; the joints were fitted so closely as to be scarcely discernible. Where the volcanic silex could not be had, other hard stones were used instead, dressed and laid in the same way; occasionally the surface of the road was made of concrete; on some of the roads, blocks of schistose stone were laid on edge, like Belgian block, as was done on a portion of the Fosse Way in Britain; on the less important roads the surface was frequently made of gravel. In Britain, the surface was sometimes made of flint stones laid in cement on a bed of gravel.

In the vicinity of iron forges, the forge cinders were used to make the road, many instances of this being found in England. Roads surfaced with forged cinders were called *viae ferriae;* this is said to be the origin of the application in France of the term *chemins ferrés* to stone roads; possibly the use in England of the word " metal " to signify the broken stone used in road making may have a similar origin.

The surface of the road was generally crowned; the principal roads were as much as fifteen or sixteen feet wide; in the vicinity of Rome they were even wider and were provided with sidewalks (*margines*). Outside of the city, these "margines" were often laid with gravel, while, inside the city, rectangular slabs of travertine were used. Narrower roads were common; Procopius, writing in the sixth century, speaks with admiration of the Appian Way being broad enough to permit wagons to pass, going in opposite directions. On some of the Alpine roads, such as that over the Julier pass, the roadway was but six feet wide, with passing places at intervals.

It was the general practice of the Romans, in locating their roads, to avoid excavation as much as possible, preferring to increase the gradients of the declivities; consequently there was no attempt to balance cuts and fills, as in modern practice, and the material for embankments was taken from borrow pits at the side of the road.

When the natural slope of the ground was too steep to carry an embankment, retaining walls were built; on rocky slopes the roadway was occasionally supported on arches. When the embankment was very high it was often retained within two walls, a notable instance being at Aricia on the Appian Way, where there is a levee over six hundred feet long and thirty-six feet high, with peperino side walls, pierced by three arched culverts.

The Roman engineers laid out their roads as straight as possible, not breaking the line for very considerable differences in elevation; this practice was continued in France until the eighteenth century. When changes in direction occurred they were generally made on high ground, or at the station houses; curves were rarely used and connecting curves at intersections were, if used at all, of very short radius. Leger mentions a curve of twenty-five feet radius, on a Roman road near Annecy, on a fifteen per cent grade, in a rock cut less than eleven feet wide. Unfortunately the Romans, whose transportation facilities were limited to pack horses and vehicles of small capacity, did not appreciate the disavantage of heavy grades, and they used gradients of ten and twelve per cent on the most ordinary occasions, and even as much as fifteen or twenty per cent, not only on mountain roads but in such places as the approach to bridges; in many cases these heavy grades have been the cause of the abandonment of Roman roads.

The practice of avoiding excavation and raising the roadway on embankment above the level of the surrounding country was carried so far in Britain that the roads were usually on embankment even at the summits; some of the English archaeologists have surmised that this was done in order to avoid surprise to marching troops. The suggestion may, however, be hazarded that the controlling reason was to avoid blockade by snow in winter, almost sure to occur in a cutting, however slight, while roads on embankment are generally free of snow.

The remarkable straightness of the Roman roads has given rise to much discussion, for while straightness is a prevailing characteristic, the Roman roads are not invariably straight, and not all straight roads are Roman. There is such good reason for preferring straight roads, that it is surprising to find a well-known writer seriously asserting that the Romans were compelled to build their roads straight because " in their ignorance of mechanics " they made their wagons with the front axle rigidly attached to the wagon body and consequently were unable readily to turn

a bend in the road.[12] It would be difficult to
prove or to disprove this assertion by reference
to any Roman wagon actually preserved; but
Sir William Gell's *Pompeiana,* published in
England in 1832, contains a reproduction of a
mural painting found at Pompeii, which shows
a four-wheeled wagon with a cut-under body,
precisely as if intended to accommodate a
swivelling axle. It is difficult to believe that so
practical a people as the Romans would use
wagons that could not readily be turned. W. W.
Mooney in his book, *Travel Among the Ancient
Romans* (Boston, 1920) pp. 86–106, shows
illustrations of wagons which could be turned.

One of the best examples of the general
straightness of the Roman roads and their
adherence to the general alignment is found in
the Fosse Way between Lincoln and Axminster
in England, where, in a distance of two hundred miles, the greatest departure from the
straight line between the two points is but six
miles; on the other hand the road from Lincoln
to York makes a detour before crossing the
Humber, that adds seventeen miles to its
length, the air line distance being fifty-five
miles.

Many of the old pavements have been worn

into grooves by the wheels that have passed over them; these grooves are so nearly at the same distance apart in the streets of Pompeii and on the Watling street in England as to give rise to the suggestion that the gauge of the Roman cart wheels fixed the gauge of the English wagon; and this in turn fixed the gauge adopted by Stephenson for his railways. Even if this cannot be positively asserted, it is at least possible; what could better show our dependence on the past than the possibility that the gauge of a little Roman cart eighteen centuries ago may have determined the gauge of our modern locomotives ?

The *Notitia* and the *Curiosum* list twenty-nine *viae*. These are not all great highways, and the list includes intersecting roads and branches. Proverbially, all roads led to Rome or radiated from it. They led to the south, to the Adriatic, to the northeast and the northwest. In Rome, at the west end of the Forum, stood the *milliarium aureum,* a column, covered with gilt bronze, originally set up by Augustus, upon which were engraved, as time went on, the names of the principal cities of the empire and their distances from Rome. It was at this point that Otho met his conspirators and was

hailed as emperor by Praetorian soldiers, at the
time of the revolt against Galba. Galba had
been offering sacrifices at the temple of Apollo
on the Palatine Hill; Otho left him, engaged in
sacred rites and prayers, and passing through
the palace of Tiberius, proceeded to the
Velabrum, and from there to the *milliarium
aureum*, near the shrine of Saturn, as Tacitus
(*Hist.*, I. 27) tells us, — there *consalutatum
imperatorem !*

Via Appia. This, the first of the great roads,
was built in 312 B.C. by the same Appius
Claudius who constructed the Appian aqueduct.

Et censura clara eo anno App. Claudii et C.
Plautii fuit, memoriae tamen felicioris ad posteros
nomen Appii, quod viam munivit et aquam in urbem
duxit; eaque unus perfecit.

The censorship of Appius Claudius and of Gaius
Plautius was notable that year; but the name of
Appius was of happier memory with posterity,
because he built a highway and also constructed an
aqueduct, leading into the city; these works he
carried out himself (Liv., IX. 29. 5).

Nearly four hundred years afterwards Statius
called it the "Queen of Roads," *longarum
regina viarum* (*Silv.*, II. 2. 12), and it was in

perfect condition when Procopius wrote in the sixth century. Based on a statement of Livy, (XLI. 27. 5), the claim has been made that roads in the city were not paved with lava (*silice stratae*), and outside the city were not paved with gravel (*glarea*) until 174 B.C.:

Censores vias sternendas silice in urbe, glarea extra urbem substruendas marginandasque primi omnium locaverunt.

This is indeed possible, but Middleton is of the opinion that the gravel was used for the sidewalks which were afterwards paved with flagstones. At some date, however, lava blocks, polygonal in shape, were employed for the paving of this important thoroughfare. Such material lay at hand in great quantities, quarried from the great stream that had flowed from the Alban Hills to within three miles of Rome; for that matter this material is still used for paving of streets in Rome, today. As originally built the Appian Way terminated at Capua; it was extended to Beneventum, probably about 280 B.C., and afterwards to Venusia, in Apulia, and to Tarentum and Brundisium in Calabria; Popilius, who was consul, 132 B.C., continued it to Rhegium, located at the south-western extremity of Italy, in Bruttium, under the name of the *Via Popilia*. The lava pavement was laid to Brundisium under Trajan. For a great part of its course it still retains its ancient pavement, but the modern Appian Way in some places deviates from the old. From Rome to Tarracina, in southern Latium, it follows almost a direct course with but three alignments connected by easy curves, crossing the Alban Hills with steep gradients and cutting across the Pomptine marshes. At Tarracina, the rocky point of Monte St. Angelo is cut back for a distance of one hundred and twenty feet for the improvement of the alignment, but this was probably done many years after the original construction. In the vicinity of Rome stone seats were provided along the roadside for pedestrians, and, as is well known, tombs were erected along the road for miles beyond the city. Julius Caesar was at one time the Curator of the Via Appia, and, as Plutarch tells us, he expended vast sums of his own money upon the improvement of the road (Plut., *Caes.*, 5). The Appian Way passed through the Porta Capena of the " Servian Wall," and through the Porta Appia of the later Wall of Aurelian. It passed through

[119]

Aricia, Lanuvium and Tarracina, on the way
to Capua; Beneventum was but a short distance, east, and Venusia, the next important
town on the way.

Via Latina. This road branched off from
the Appian Way about half a mile east of the
Porta Capena, and passed through the Porta
Latina of the Aurelian Wall, a short distance
north from the Porta Appia. It continued its
course through the centre of Latium, affording
a second great highway toward the south. It
rejoined the Appian Way a short distance north
of Capua, at Casilinum, thus making an alternate route into Campania. The Via Latina was
probably one of the earliest roads of Italy, being built shortly after the Appian Way.

A veritable network of roads eventually led
from Rome, crossing Latium in every direction.
Besides those already mentioned, there were
the Via Labicana, leading to Labici; Via
Gabina òr Praenestina, communicating with
Gabii and Praeneste; Via Tiburtina, connecting
Rome with Tibur; the Via Salaria and the Via
Flaminia, leading to the north, and running on
either side of the Tiber; the Via Cornelia and
the Via Aurelia, leading into Etruria; the Via
Portuensis, running parallel to and north of the

Tiber, on the right bank, to Portus Augusti, on the coast of Latium; and the Via Ostiensis running parallel to the river and south of it (on the left bank) to Ostia.

The *Via Labicana* branched off from the Via Praenestina, after the latter had passed through the Porta Praenestina. The Via Labicana ran south of the Via Praenestina.

The *Via Tiburtina* passed through the Porta Tiburtina, and it was extended, under the name of Via Valeria, to the Adriatic, going quite directly east to Aternum (now Pescara); thence it proceeded up the coast, joining the Via Salaria. It had several branches, one of which, called the Via Sublacensis, led up the valley of the Anio, where so many aqueducts had their sources. Another branch, called the Collatina, left the Via Tiburtina at the Porta Tiburtina and led, eastward, to Collatia, being used for local traffic only. It is not even mentioned in the regionary catalogues.

The *Via Salaria* led into the Sabine country and owed its name to the salt traffic which proceeded along this road into the interior:

Salaria via Romae est appellata, quia per eam Sabini sal a mari deferebant (Fest., 327 M = p. 437, Lindsay Edition).

The older road, the Via Salaria vetus, passed through a gate of the " Servian " wall in the Quirinal Hill, either the Porta Salutaris or the Porta Quirinalis, thence through the Porta Pinciana of the Aurelian Wall; but the Via Salaria nova began at the old Porta Collina of the " Servian " Wall and passed through the Porta Salaria of the Aurelian Wall, joining the old road, beyond. The Via Salaria proceeded northward, east of the Tiber; it passed through Reate, of the Sabine district; under Augustus, it was extended to the Adriatic, to Truentum; from Truentum it followed the coastline northward to Ancona, where it joined the Via Flaminia.

The *Via Flaminia* was first built by C. Flaminius, who was either censor or consul in 223 B.C.,

C. Flaminius censor viam Flaminiam muniit et circum Flaminium exstruxit. (Liv., *Epit.*, XX.),

and it led to Ariminum. Beginning in Rome, at the old Porta Fontinalis of the " Servian " Wall, it passed northward through the Campus Martius, being called the Via Lata (or " Broadway ") from the Capitol to the Porticus of Agrippa. It passed through the Porta Flaminia of the Wall of Aurelian, crossed the Tiber, passed through southern Etruria, west of the Tiber, going through Falerii, crossed the river again, and entered Umbria and proceeded thence on its long and mountainous journey to Ariminum. As we read in the *Monumentum Ancyranum,* it was reconstructed by Augustus:

Consul septimum viam Flaminiam ab urbe Ariminum feci . . . (*Mon. Anc.,* IV. 19.)

It crossed the Apennines by a pass eight hundred metres high. The road was extended from Ariminum to Placentia, in Cisalpine Gaul, as the *Via Aemilia,* in 187 B.C.; from Placentia it led to Mediolanum (or Milan). Pliny the Younger gives us an interesting reference to this road, when he writes: " I was taking holiday at Comum, when I heard that Cornutus Tertullus was appointed Curator of the Aemilian Way " (*Epist.,* V. 14. 1). He adds expressions of great pleasure that Cornutus should have received this honor. Pliny himself served as *curator alvei Tiberis et riparum et cloacarum urbis.* The Aemilian Way was also extended along the coast line of the Adriatic from Ariminum to Aquileia by a road called the *Via Popilia,* which was built by Popilius in 132 B.C.

From Ariminum, also, a branch led south to Ancona.

The *Viae Cornelia* and *Aurelia* were two highways leading into Etruria. The former left Rome at the pons Aelius, while the latter began at the pons Aemilius. The Aurelian Way ascended the Janiculum and passed through the porta Aurelia of the Aurelian Wall. It followed the coast line, going through Caere, Tarquinii, Populonia, Pisa, Luna, on its way to Genoa, whence it proceeded by the Riviera and the maritime Alps to southern Gaul and Spain. It owed its name to its builder, Aurelius Cotta (242 B.C.). It was connected with the Via Aemilia by a road to Placentia called the Via Postumia, built in 148 B.C.

The *Viae Portuensis* and *Ostiensis,* as has been said, led to the sea. The former passed through the porta Portuensis, and the latter through the porta Ostiensis of the Aurelian Wall. The latter turned to the south from Ostia, and under the name of Via Severiana led along the coast to Tarracina, where it joined the Appian Way.

Besides these great highways, there were many others, such as the Via Asinaria and the Via Tusculana, the Via Nomentana, which led to Nomentum in Latium, the Ardeatina, connecting Rome with Ardea, the Via Cassia, also called the Via Clodia, in reality two branches of one road that started at Rome, but which, by the one branch (Cassia) led to Arretium, thence to Florentia and Pistoria, and by the other (Clodia) led to northwestern Etruria, joining the Aurelian way on the coast.

Silvius draws a most interesting sketch of a road in the building and indicates the importance of these roads clearly enough in the *Silvae* (IV. 3). The Via Domitiana was being built from Sinuessa to Naples, along the coast, replacing an old and very bad road, and Statius says:

" 'Tis he (Domitian) who, brooking ill the slow journeys of his people and the plains that clog every minute of the road, sweeps away tedious windings and lays a new solid paving upon the weary sands, rejoicing to bring the Euboean Sibyl's home . . . and sweltering Baiae nearer to the seven hills " (vss. 20–26 Mozley trans., in *The Loeb Library*), and, later,

Haec amnis pariterque se levarat | ingenti plaga marmorata dorso,

" Thus spoke the river and therewith a marbled stretch of roadway had arisen with mighty ridge " (vss. 95, 96).

[125]

Between Naples and Puteoli a road passed through a fine rock-cut tunnel, about half a mile long, nearly thirty feet wide, and twenty-five to thirty feet high.

In this brief sketch of roads, mention should at least be made of the exhaustive studies of the Campagna by Tomassetti and Ashby, which are invaluable for students of Roman monuments, including aqueducts and roads.[13] Imagination can easily reconstruct the life, military, commercial, and social, that called these roads into being, and which at one time made them vital arteries of the *corpus Romanum* or of the *civitas Romana*.

In the location of mountain roads the Roman engineers appear to have taken pains to select favorable passes for crossing the ridges, and to have made careful projection of the routes; they also reduced the gradients by making appropriate developments and thus increasing the length of the line, while at the same time adhering closely to their well-known principle of keeping the line as straight as the topography would permit.

The principal Alpine passes over which the Romans constructed roads are as follows: [14]

Mt. Genèvre, in the Cottian Alps, on the road

from Milan to Arles; the road was built in 75 B.C., and was used in 58 B.C. by Caesar on his way to the Gallic War. The Monte Genèvre was probably the pass by which Hannibal crossed the Alps. Besides Arles the road communicated by branches with Valencia and Vienne, on the Rhone; this was the most frequented of all the Alpine routes.

Between Mt. Genèvre and the Little St. Bernard is the Mt. Cenis, said to have been crossed by Hasdrubal and over which Pompey is said to have made a road, afterwards abandoned; the road is still known by the name of *La Strada Romana*.

The Little St. Bernard, in the Graian Alps, on the road from Milan to Vienne on the Rhone, was the principal pass over the Alps into *Gallia Comata,* before the road over Mt. Genèvre was opened in 75 B.C.; this was the one crossed by Caesar when he returned from Gaul to Rome just before the civil war, 49 B.C. The road has been traced for a great part of its length. The Little St. Bernard, the Mt. Cenis, and Mt. Genèvre are rival claimants for the honor of being the route taken by Hannibal.

The Great St. Bernard, in the Pennine Alps, is the oldest of the Alpine roads. It is said to have been used in the time of the Tarquins. The road diverges from the route over the Little St. Bernard at Aosta. It has been traced for a part of its length, but in many places it has disappeared. Near the summit is a rock-cutting two hundred feet long with a road bed about twelve feet wide. At the summit are the remains of an old Roman *statio* or *mansio;* and a museum containing many Roman relics. On the Italian side the road ascends to the summit in zigzags of two or three hundred feet. Napoleon led his army over this route in 1800, and parts of the old road are still in use as a local road.

The Simplon pass in the Helvetian Alps is said to have been known to the Romans, as also the St. Gotthard, but the extent of their use or of the construction of a road over either pass is doubtful.

The San Bernardino pass in the Raetian Alps, formed one of three routes from Milan to Coira; the road ascends the valley of the Mesocco, then descends the valley of the Hinter Rhine to Coira; portions of the road have been preserved and near the sources of the Rhine are the remains of a Roman temple.

The route over the Splügen passed from Milan by Lake Como, and ascended the valley of the Mera to Chiavenna, and the valley of San Giacomo to the summit, then descends to join the San Bernardino route in the valley of the Hinter Rhine. Some portions of the road-bed have been found.

The route over the Septimer pass diverged from that over the Splügen at Chiavenna, thence continuing up the valley of the Mera to the summit, descended the valley of the Oberhalbstein. A portion of the road has been found. This was a better route than the San Bernardino and the Splügen, as it avoided the narrow chasm of the *Via Mala* in the Valley of the Hinter Rhine, through which passed the road from both of those passes; although by its better location on higher ground the Roman road along the Hinter Rhine was less exposed to danger from avalanche and flood than the modern road.

The road over the Julier pass left the Septimer route at Casaccia and then crossing Mt. Julier descended the valleys of the Albula and the Hinter Rhine to Coira; a branch road diverged before crossing the summit, and keeping to the right passed through the Engadine and followed the valley of the Inn to Vindelicia and Pannonia.

The Reschenscheideck in the Noric Alps was the pass on the route from Verona to the valley of the Inn; the road was built by Drusus the stepson of Augustus in 15 B.C. It ascended the valley of the Adige, through Trent, to the Reschenscheideck range which separated the Adige from the Inn.

The Brenner pass made a more direct route, leaving the Reschenscheideck route at the confluence of the Adige and the Eisach rivers, and, ascending the latter to the summit at the Brenner pass, thence it descended the valley of the Sill to the River Inn at Innsbruck, and proceeded thence to Augsburg.

There was also the great military road, the Via Egnatia, from Trieste through Istria to Thessalonica and Byzantium, dating probably from the conquest of Macedonia, 146 B.C. This was the principal highway to the east. Also from Trieste, ran Trajan's great road through Laibach and the Save valley to the Danube near Belgrade; thence descending the Danube to its mouth, it passed through the Iron Gate, not far from the site of Trajan's famous bridge, by a half tunnel cut in the face of the precipitous cliff. This tunnel is described by Duruy as but five feet wide, the roadway being widened by a timber platform extending outwards over the river. A branch from this road reached Adrianople and Byzantium.

In several places where the ancient and modern roads have been constructed over the same general route, comparisons have been made, not always favorable to the modern. The Roman road over the Julier takes the summit in fewer zigzags than the modern road and is said to be less exposed to the wind. The Roman road over the Bernardino is used in winter and spring in preference to the modern road, which is frequently blockaded by snow drifts which the Roman road avoided by its better location; [15] it would appear that in making their location the Roman engineers had taken meteorological features of the mountains into account as well as the topography.

It is probable that in none of the provinces have the roads played a more important part in the early development and subsequent history of the people than in Britain. The original Celtic inhabitants of Britain were great horsemen, famous for their war chariots with scythe blades attached to the axles; one form of the

[131]

British two-wheeled carriage was adopted and largely used by the Romans after the conquest of Britain; such a people must have had roads, and many of the British archaeologists have thought that portions of some of the great Roman roads in England were originally British roads, improved, and in some instances, paved, by the Romans; but Dr. Guest was of the opinion that there is no reason to believe that the Britons had constructed any artificial or paved roads before the arrival of the Romans, and Professor Haverfield considers it doubtful whether any of the Roman roads follow lines laid out by the British. In a general way, the British roads, being unpaved, appear now, when they can be recognized, as a ditch, while the Roman roads appear ordinarily as an embankment. Leger calls attention to the same distinction in France, where the Gallic roads are often sunk twelve or fifteen feet in the ground; the Gallic roads are also irregular in their alignment, winding round the hills, while the Roman roads are broader, irregular in profile, with long straight alignments, and with the road surface always crowned.

Four of the ancient highways of Britain have acquired special historical prominence, and have been known since Norman and even Saxon times as "The Four Roman Ways," although there were many other roads undoubtedly Roman, and although the Roman origin of one of them and of a part of another has been disputed. These roads are the Watling Street, the Ermine Street, the Fosse Way, and the Icknield Way; besides being the most important roads of the kingdom, they derived an additional importance from the fact that under the laws of Edward the Confessor, renewed by William the Conqueror, they were proclaimed Royal Highways, and as such, offenses committed on these roads were removed from the jurisdiction of the county courts, and tried in the King's courts; this privilege was extended to all the principal highways of the kingdom in the twelfth century. The importance of these as well as of other Roman roads in the development of the country is also indicated by their being in many cases the boundary lines between counties and townships. The Watling Street bounds Warwickshire for twenty-two miles, and similar instances occur throughout the kingdom.

The first of these roads, the Watling Street, commenced at Dover, and led by way of Canterbury and Rochester to the Thames near London, the London street, called Watling Street, being perhaps a detour from the main road for the convenience of passengers desiring to pass through the capital city. From London, it passed west of St. Albans, through Stratford to Wroxeter and Chester, and thence through North Wales to the coast. A branch led to York and beyond to the Tyne and Scotland, the road leading north from York being frequently called Watling Street. North of the Tyne it was known as Dere Street. There are several other roads in England called Watling Street that do not appear to have had any connection with the Watling Street that passes through London. Watling Street in Kent is the road by which Chaucer's Canterbury pilgrims travelled on their way to Canterbury.

The Ermine Street ran northward from London to Lincoln, *via* Huntingdon; owing to the absence of Roman remains and to its omission in the Itineraries of Antoninus, the Roman origin of the Ermine Street between London and Huntingdon has been disputed. The argument from the Itineraries may be met by the reasonable supposition that the Ermine Street north of Huntingdon was constructed before the Itineraries were compiled, and the road south of Huntingdon afterward, perhaps but a little while before the Romans left Britain; this supposition would also account for the absence of Roman relics. In short, the argument for the non-Roman origin of the southern part of the Ermine Street, although supported by the weight of Dr. Guest's authority, does not appear conclusive. Mr. Codrington in his *Roman Roads in Britain* states that the evidence on the ground is quite to the contrary, and that the Ermine Street from London to Godmanchester, near Huntingdon, possesses the characteristic features of a Roman road.

Dr. Guest derives the name, Ermine Street, from the Saxon, " street of the Fen-men "; the road from Huntingdon to Lincoln passing through the country of the fens and marshes, where the Romans began their great drainage works which the English completed in the nineteenth century.

The Fosse Way ran from Lincoln through Leicester, Cirencester, and Bath to Cornwall, and was extended northward to Caithness, the extreme point of Scotland; north of Lincoln to the Humber it is known as the High Street.

The word " fosse " properly signifies a

trench, but was applied indifferently to a canal or to a road, not inappropriately, as the Roman road was laid in a trench; the word dyke has a similar double meaning, a ditch in Lincolnshire and an embankment elsewhere.

The Icknield Street starts from a point in Suffolk in the country of the Iceni, the British tribe of which Boudicca was queen in the rebellion of A.D. 62; thence proceeding westward it passed about ten miles south of Cambridge and Oxford, connecting with the roads to the southwest.

Dr. Guest and other authorities are of the opinion that the Icknield Street is not a Roman road, basing their opinion on the fact that nowhere on its route is there any indication of a paved highway. Probably it was not; but in any case, it was no doubt much used in Roman times as the principal road from east to west, and its prominence is sufficiently indicated by its inclusion in the " Four Roman Ways."

The Watling Street and the Fosse Way are certainly Roman from end to end, and so also is the Ermine Street between Lincoln and Huntingdon, if not for its entire length; these roads are said to have remained in good condition until the twelfth century. They are now almost entirely destroyed, due principally to the taking of the stone for use in building new roads in the eighteenth and nineteenth centuries, just as the Roman builders took the stones of Marcia to build Felice.

English archaeologists have noted the coincidence of the location of the Roman roads in Britain with the location of the principal modern highways and railways. While this coincidence is in great part to be accounted for by topographical considerations, it is none the less remarkable that the Roman engineers in an undeveloped and heavily wooded country should, in locating their main lines of communication, have anticipated so closely the general outline of the modern railway systems.

The Romans were well acquainted with the curative properties of the waters of Bath, and the constant travel between London and Bath was taken care of by a road connecting with the Watling Street at Verulam, and running thence to Bath by way of Cirencester; as many of the travellers were invalids, the Saxons gave the road the appropriate name of Akeman Street, and the town of Bath they called Akemanceaster.

During the reign of Augustus, the *Cursus*

Publicus or governmental mail and courier service, which had been inaugurated in republican times, was extended to the principal roads of the empire. " Stations " were established where relays of horses and carriages were kept ready at all times for the Emperor's messengers, and for others who were authorized by imperial *diploma,* or passport, to make use of the government service. These *stationes* were of three classes, *stativae,* or *civitates* at important stopping places and at the principal cities; *mansiones,* from thirty to forty miles apart, where travellers could be lodged over night and procure necessary supplies; and *mutationes,* or relay stations ten or twelve miles apart, where fresh horses could be had; at the *mansiones* carriages and horses could usually be hired. The use of the government service was strictly confined to the properly authorized officials and the issue of *diplomata* was under the personal direction of the Emperor; private citizens had to rely upon their own resources or avail themselves of hired conveyances or messengers. Associations or guilds of those engaged in the business of supplying vehicles and messenger service were formed in many of the cities in the period of the Republic, and in the second century A.D. private forwarding companies were organized for the purpose of carrying letters, and no doubt parcels as well, thus foreshadowing our modern express and forwarding companies. The station-masters, or " stationers," no doubt kept writing materials on hand for the accommodation of travellers, and the word stationery is still in use to signify such supplies; this being one of the thousand little things that indicate how closely we are connected with our Roman predecessors. With their smoothly paved roads and the efficient management of the relay stations, very rapid progress was often made. It is said that Tiberius when sent by Augustus to Germany covered two hundred miles in twenty-four hours with five changes of chariots. The *Cursus Publicus* played an important part in the career of Constantine the Great, who was enabled by its use to be with his dying father at York, where Constantine was proclaimed Emperor.

Several of Pliny's interesting letters to Trajan refer to the *Cursus Publicus* and the issue of diplomas; in one of them Pliny asks the Emperor's indulgence for his issuing, without first obtaining the Emperor's permission, a diploma to his wife, who had been suddenly called home by the death of her grandfather, the urgency of the occasion not admitting the delay which waiting for the Emperor's permission would have caused. Of course Trajan replied in that kind and sympathetic way which was peculiarly his own; we do not usually look for kindness and sympathy in Roman Emperors, but this was Trajan, the good Emperor, whose act of justice and beneficence to the poor friendless widow was the theme of mediaeval legend and of Dante's verse.[16]

After the fall of the Empire, conditions differed in the different provinces; in Italy, where Theodoric had expressed his determination to continue the Roman tradition and to restore Italy, wasted by war, there was less disorganization than in some of the provinces; for a time engineering work was not altogether discontinued, public buildings were repaired, the aqueducts restored, the roads kept in repair, and the operation of the *Cursus Publicus* continued.

In Gaul, especially in southern Gaul, where the Romanization of the people had the most progressed, the Visigoths had themselves been brought under the influence of Roman civilization, and were actuated by the same motives as had inspired Theodoric; but both in Gaul and in Italy, the breaking up of the unified system of government, and, later, the introduction of the feudal system, were not favorable to the construction of new works, nor even to the proper maintenance of the old.

In France, the roads were kept in what Hilaire Belloc has described as " declining repair " until the time of Charlemagne, who, like the Romans, had large armies; but under his successors, the roads were generally neglected, so that in France, as in England, it is said that until the twelfth century, there were no roads except those made by the Romans.

In the seventeenth century road building was revived in France under the direction of Colbert, minister of finance under Louis XIV; with some modifications, the Roman type of road was retained, the foundations being made of heavy stones laid in a trench, but the total thickness of the structure was reduced to one and a half or two and a half feet.

In 1765–75, Trésaguet, who was in France what Telford and Macadam were in England, introduced a further modification, reducing the thickness of the road metal to about ten inches, the depth being uniform over the entire width

[141]

of the roadway, the subgrade being given the same crowning as the surface. Trésaguet relied on thorough drainage and constant repair for the maintenance of the road; the Romans relied on the indestructibility of the original construction. Trésaguet's type of road was universally used in France until superseded by the methods of Telford and Macadam.

In England, the relapse under the Saxons from the civilization which the country enjoyed under the Romans, was more marked than in France, and the recovery was slower. The old Roman roads which had been sufficient for the Saxons and Normans, and which are said to have remained in good condition until the eleventh or twelfth century, had become inadequate, and beside them no paved roads had been built. Most of the travelling was on horseback, very few people riding in carriages, which were usually without springs, and a long journey was something to be avoided, even when the roads were passable.

No permanent improvement was made until the eighteenth century, when Metcalfe, whom Smiles calls the first of the English road-makers, undertook the construction of nearly two hundred miles of improved roadway. Strangely enough, Metcalfe, who laid out and supervised the construction of these roads, was blind, — " Blind Jock of Knaresborough." Sir Walter Scott had him in mind when he drew the character of Wandering Willie in *Redgauntlet*.

Sixty years after Metcalfe, Telford and Macadam built the roads that have made them famous. They abandoned the heavy structure of the Romans, and adopted a simpler method of construction, perfectly adequate for their time but deficient in strength and durability for the heavy and rapidly moving traffic of the twentieth century, which demands a heavier body and a more durable surface than Telford, Macadam, and Trésaguet had found necessary, and which may ultimately compel a return to a more solid construction, resembling that of the Romans while avoiding their excessive use of material. The importance of depth of structure in diminishing the unit stress on the underlying subsoil by a better distribution of the pressure is more generally recognized, and foundations of solid concrete, resembling the Roman *statumen* and *rudus*, are now usually specified for roads intended for heavy traffic.[17]

VII. BRIDGES AND TUNNELS

THE Romans early in their history began the construction of bridges over the Tiber and on the lines of their roads.

The first bridge over the Tiber,[18] of which we have record, was the Pons Sublicius. According to tradition, it was built by the king, Ancus Marcius:

Ianiculum quoque adiectum, non inopia loci, sed ne quando ea arx hostium esset. Id non muro solum, sed etiam ob commoditatem itineris ponte Sublicio, tum primum in Tiberim facto, coniugi urbi placuit. (Liv., I. 33. 6.)

The Janiculum hill was annexed to the city, not for want of room, but that the enemy might not seize it and use it for a citadel. It was determined to join it to the city not only by a wall, but for the greater ease of passing to and fro, by means of the Sublician bridge, then for the first time built across the Tiber.

Other ancient authorities agree in this tradition. While Plutarch also says that it was

built by Ancus Marcius, he further tells us that
" the custody and maintenance of the bridge,
like all the other inviolable and ancestral rites,
were attached to the priesthood (i.e., the pon-
tiffs), for the Romans held the demolition of
the wooden bridge to be not only unlawful, but
actually sacrilegious. It is also said that it was
built entirely without iron and fastened together with wooden pins. . . . The stone
bridge was constructed at a much later date,
when Aemilius was quaestor."

(Plut., *Numa,* 9, tr. of Perrin, in the *Loeb* Series.)

Pliny the Elder tells us of buildings in the
ancient world, constructed without the use of
iron (nails), and adds:

quod item Romae in ponte sublicio religiosum est
(Pliny, *N.H.,* XXXVI. 15. 23. 100)
as at Rome, on religious grounds, in the case of the
Sublician bridge.

The name *sublicius* (resting on piles) is derived from *sublica,* meaning a stake or a pile,
and the bridge was, certainly, originally constructed wholly of wood, without the use of
metal. Of course we recall Caesar's use of the
word *sublica,* used in his account of the bridge

that he built across the Rhine. He drove pairs of logs, a foot and a half thick, into the bed of the stream; these two logs (of each pair), two feet apart, were fastened together but did not stand perpendicularly in the stream:

non sublicae modo derecte ad perpendiculum, (*De B. G.*, IV. 17),
not vertically, like a pile,

but they slanted a little, in the direction of the current.

It was on the Sublician bridge that Horatius Cocles fought so valiantly against the Etruscans and Lars Porsena of Clusium, in the year 508 B.C. At the end of the combat, as he leaped into the river, he uttered the famous prayer to Father Tiber to receive him and his arms and to protect him. It was still a wooden bridge in the time of Augustus. Ovid describes the ceremony of Argei, which included throwing rush-puppets into the Tiber, and he says:

Tum quoque priscorum virgo simulacra virorum
  Mittere *roboreo* scirpea ponte solet, (*Fasti*, V. 621–22).
At that time, the Vestal throws (into the Tiber) the images of men of old,

[146]

The images of rushes from the wooden *bridge, she
throws.*

Seneca also refers to the bridge, by the old
name:

In sublicium pontem me transfer et inter egentes
abige: non ideo tamen me despiciam, quod in illo-
rum numero consedero, qui manum ad stipem
porrigunt. (*De V. Beata,* 25. 1.)

Put me on the Sublician bridge and drive me out
among the beggars; I shall not on that account de-
spise myself because I shall be seated among those
who hold out their hand for alms.

But Servius, writing in the fourth century
A.D., describing the combat of Horatius on the
bridge, says:

et cum (Porsena) per sublicium pontem, hoc est
ligneum, qui modo lapideus dicitur, transire co-
naretur, solus Cocles hostilem impetum sus-
tinuit . . . (Serv., *Aen.*, VIII. 646).

and when (Porsena) endeavored to cross the Sublician bridge, i.e. the wooden bridge, which is now
called the *stone* bridge, Cocles alone met the attack
of the enemy.

It is possible that the wooden bridge had in
part or in whole been reconstructed of stone
at that late date or, perhaps, earlier. Tacitus

records the destruction of the bridge by a flood in the time of Vitellius and Otho.

(Tac., *Hist.*, I 86.)

A bridge called by the old name was still in existence at the time of the *Notitia* and the *Curiosum*, which catalogue the *pons Sublicius* among the bridges of Rome.

But where did the Sublician Bridge cross the Tiber ? There has been much discussion of this question, but here it will suffice to say that, in all probability, the bridge led from the area of the Forum Boarium straight across the river, below the island, and a short distance below the later Pons Aemilius.

The Pons Aemilius was begun in 179 B.C. and finished in 142 B.C. In the year 179, M. Aemilius Lepidus, a pontifex maximus, and M. Fulvius were censors. Livy tells of their public works and says:

M. Fulvius plura et maioris locavit usus, portum et pilas pontis in Tiberim, quibus pilis fornices post aliquot annos P. Scipio Africanus et L. Mummius censores locaverunt imponendos. (Livy, XL. 51, 179 B.C.)

Marcus Fulvius contracted for more works and of greater use, a place to anchor ships on the Tiber and piers for a bridge across the river; P. Scipio

Africanus and L. Mummius, as censors, many years later contracted for the erection of arches on these piers.

We have already seen that Plutarch (*Numa,* 9) refers to the *stone* bridge of Aemilius.

Thus the ancient evidence for this bridge is very scanty; but it is mentioned in the *Notitia* (as we shall see) and was, therefore, still in existence in the fourth century after Christ. It is referred to, " per pontem Aemilium," in the *Life* of Heliogabalus by Lampridius (C. 17). One arch of a bridge now stands in mid-stream, below the island, and above the generally accepted location of the Sublician bridge and, by a process of elimination, this arch, called the " ponte Rotto " since 1598, has been identified with the Aemilian bridge. At different times, in the fourth and fifth centuries A.D., this bridge was called the *pons lapideus* (lapis = stone) and *pons Lepidi;* in the Middle Ages, it went by other names, as, e.g. " pons Senatorum," as it was called in the *Mirabilia* of the twelfth century. The bridges as listed in the *Mirabilia* are:

Pons Milvius, pons Adrianus, pons Neronianus, pons Antoninus, pons Fabricius, pons Gratianus, pons. Senatorum, pons marmoreus Theodosii, et pons Valentinianus. (*Mirabilia,* 11, cf. p. 617 Jordan, *Topographie,* II.)

The Aemilian bridge cannot be identified with any other bridge in the list (cf. F. M. Nichols' translation of the *Mirabilia,* p. 24). The piers of this bridge were badly located to resist floods, and, after the damage done to the bridge in 1598, it was never repaired.

There were two bridges connecting the city with the island, the one from the left bank to the island, called the *pons Fabricius,* the one from the island to the right bank, the *pons Cestius.* The pons Fabricius was built of tufa and peperino, and it had travertine facing; it was carried by two stone semicircular arches, with an arched opening in the central pier, which was probably provided for the purpose of affording an additional waterway in case of floods. Another arch is built into the modern embankment on the left side, where the modern level of the streets is considerably above the ancient level. The bridge is still standing and no important restorations have been necessary since the first construction. Over the arches appears the following inscription:

L. FABRICIUS C. F. CUR. VIAR.

FACIUNDUM COERAVIT

[150]

i.e., Lucius Fabricius, son of Gaius, *curator viarum*, commissioner of roads, was responsible for the building; and over the smaller, central arch appears the legend:

EIDEMQUE
PROBAVEIT

i.e., the same man guaranteed the work. This was in 62 B.C. Another inscription, appearing on either side of the bridge, testifies that the work was again approved in 21 B.C.

Q. LEPIDUS . . .M. LOLLIUS . . .
EX S. C. PROBAVERUNT

Q. Lepidus and M. Lollius, in accordance with a decree of the senate, approved (*C. I. L.* vi., 1305–1. 600). The bridge is, today, called the "ponte dei Quattro Capi" from the four-headed *hermae* that once were a part of the decorations of a parapet; the present parapet is modern and only two of the ancient *hermae* are left in position. In the Middle Ages, it bore the name of *pons Judaeorum*, because of its proximity to the Ghetto.

Both the Fabrician and Cestian bridges are mentioned by their ancient names in the *Notitia*. The pons Cestius is, today, called "ponte di

S. Bartolomeo." It is a typical Roman stone bridge and was built about the same time as the *pons Fabricius*, approximately between 72 and 44 B.C. It was restored a number of times, as in A.D. 370 when it was re-named "pons Gratiani," again in the eleventh century, and later, in 1886–89. Three arches appear, the central one of which is ancient, of the year 370.

Livy tells of prodigies that terrified Rome in the year 192 B.C. and he speaks of a destructive flood:

Tiberis infestiore quam priore anno impetu illatus urbi duos pontes, aedificia multa, maxime circa Flumentanam portam, evertit. (XXXV. 21. 5.)

The Tiber pouring over the city with more destructive force than in the previous year, destroyed *two bridges,* and many buildings, especially those near the porta Flumentana.

This cannot refer to the Aemilian bridge, which was not yet built, nor does it appear to refer to the *pons Sublicius*. A bridge connected the left bank of the Tiber with the island as early as 291 B.C., when the cult of Aesculapius was established there. The passage in Livy is thought to refer to early wooden bridges, connecting the city with the island.

About 100 metres below the *pons Aelius*, there are remains of piers of a bridge, which must be identified as the *pons Neronianus*. These piers are visible at low water and can hardly belong to any other bridge. The bridge is not mentioned in the *Notitia*, so we can assume that it was not in existence at that time. A " pons Neronianus " is mentioned by name, in the *Mirabilia*, and any bridge of Nero's must, almost certainly, have been built where the piers I have just referred to, still are. Such a bridge would facilitate passage from the Campus Martius to the gardens of Agrippina and to the Circus Gai, on the other side of the river, and Nero's name is closely associated with this circus in the Vatican area. It presumably was built in the latter part of Nero's reign, but the building of the *pons Aelius* either was responsible for the neglect and decay of the *pons Neronianus*, or was due to the earlier destruction of Nero's bridge.

The *pons Aelius*, also called the *pons Hadriani*, later, *pons Sancti Petri*, and now known as the " ponte S. Angelo," was finished in A.D. 134. It was built by the Emperor Hadrian to lead from the Campus Martius to the Emperor's great tomb, on the other side of the river. It consisted originally of eight arches, the three in the center being about fifty-nine feet span, with approaches of three and two smaller arches at either end, respectively. At the center the bridge was about fifty feet above the water, the approaches having an inclination of about eleven percent. This is a good example of the "dos d'ane" type of bridge, common among the Roman bridges and very generally imitated throughout Europe during the early middle ages. Two of the three arches on the left were hidden beneath an embankment, and were discovered in 1892, when the ends of the bridge were rebuilt; only the three central arches of the ancient bridge remain. The original pavement of the roadway on the approaches was still in existence in 1892. Bergier says of this bridge that it was "one of the most beautiful and magnificent works that one could see."

Because of their probably close proximity to each other, it is well to associate the *pons Agrippae* and the *pons Aurelius* and discuss them together. It is most surprising that our ancient literature does not refer to a bridge of Agrippa, assuming that the great statesman of Augustus built this bridge. Only one inscription, carved on a stone *cippus* that was found in 1877, mentions this bridge; the inscription is of the time of the Emperor Claudius and mentions the erection of stone *cippi*, on the left bank of the Tiber, from the *trigarium* (an open space in the Campus Martius, in the ninth region of the " Circus Flaminius," for the training of horses.)

AD PONTEM AGRIPPAE (*C.I.L.*, VI. 31545)

This astonishing statement received confirmation, about twelve years after the discovery of the inscription, from the discovery of remains of sunken piers, 100 metres above the *pons Aurelius*. The " bridge of Agrippa " may have been carried away by a flood early in the empire, at some time after the date of the inscription, and its existence gradually forgotten. But the piers and the inscription upon the *cippus* found near the Strada Giulia, certainly seem to complement each other and prove the existence of a bridge by this name.

The *pons Aurelius* is mentioned in the *Notitia*, but in the *Mirabilia* it is called the *pons Antoninus*. It was partially destroyed in 772, called the " pons Ruptus " until 1475, when it was rebuilt in its present shape; since that day it has been called the *ponte Sisto*. It is not known whether Marcus Aurelius first built the bridge or, as has been surmised, whether Caracalla did so. This bridge is now also commonly identified with the one called *pons Valentinianus*.

The two bridges, the *pons Agrippae* and the *pons Aurelius,* crossed the Tiber, from the Campus Martius, about half way between the island, to the south, and the *pons Neronianus* to the north. If the bridge of Agrippa had been in existence in the second century A.D., the *pons Aurelius* would hardly have been required.

The *Notitia* mentions the following bridges: Sublicius, Aemilius, Fabricius, Cestius, Aelius, Aurelius, Mulvius, and Probi. Of the bridges we have discussed, the bridges of *Agrippa* and of *Nero* are not mentioned; we have already seen that there are good reasons for thinking that they were not in existence and in use at the late date of the *Notitia* (ca. A.D. 334). But where was the "pons Probi"? Probus was Emperor from A.D. 276 to 282. This name appears in only one other place, viz., in the calendar of Polemius Silvius, the date of which is A.D. 448. If this bridge of Probus was a new bridge and not a new name given to one of the old bridges that he might have restored, the only bridge it can be identified with is a bridge of Theodosius, also called *pons marmoreus,* which spanned the Tiber below all of the other bridges, crossing the river from the Aventine side. Here, bases of piers still exist beneath the regular level of the river. These are near the area called *Marmorata,* or quay for the reception of imported marbles. The location of Theodosius' bridge explains its other name of "pons marmoreus." It was built between A.D. 381 and 387, and destroyed in 1484. Did Theodosius rebuild the bridge of Probus? This question we can hardly answer with any certainty.

The *pons Mulvius,* or the " ponte Molle," as it is called today, was several miles north of the city and it carried the Flaminian Way across the Tiber. The road was built in 220 B.C., but the first reference we have to the bridge, occurs in Livy's account of the excitement at Rome, in 207 B.C., over the news of the battle of Metaurus. One continuous train of people extended as far as the Mulvian bridge:

ad Mulvium usque pontem continens agmen per-venit. (Liv., XXVII. 51. 2.)

As is well known, it was at the Mulvian bridge that the envoys of the Allobroges who had entered into negotiations with the Catilinarian conspirators, were apprehended.

(Cic., *ad Catil.*, III. 2.5)

Tacitus says that in Nero's day, the Mulvian bridge was a haunt of vice and that Nero often went there for the sake of enjoying greater freedom. (*Ann.*, XIII. 47.)

pons Mulvius in eo tempore celebris nocturnis inlecebris erat; ventitabatque illuc Nero, quo solutius urbem extra lasciviret.

And on the day before the battle between Constantine and Maxentius, fought in A.D. 312, near the Mulvian bridge, the famous token of a cross of light appeared in the sky, with the words:

hac vince. (Eusebius, *Vita Const.*, I. 28.)

Such are the associations we have with this bridge. It was built of peperino, with travertine facing, and when Augustus re-made the Flaminian road from Rome to Ariminum, this bridge required no reconstruction, as we learn from the *Monumentum Ancyranum* (IV. 20). The bridge was restored in 1808, and four of its six arches are ancient. The spans of the arches vary from fifty-one to seventy-nine feet.

The shallow foundations of their river piers were the weak points of Roman bridge construction; many of the failures of Roman bridges were of the piers. The construction of cofferdams and subaqueous foundations was described by Vitruvius, but their facilities for pumping were too inadequate to sink their foundations to any considerable depth, and when unable to divert the stream during the construction of the piers, they resorted to a foundation of riprap, making up for the weakness of the foundation by building both foundation and pier extremely large. This in turn aggravated the danger by diminishing the waterway, a condition which they sometimes attempted to relieve by building an arched opening in the pier or in the head wall of the bridge. Arches of very long span were often used in river bridges to avoid the construction of piers in midstream.

This narrowing of the waterway by the excessive thickness of the piers was a common feature of mediaeval and early modern bridges which were generally imitations of Roman bridges. It is stated that at the old London bridge, where the tide rises and falls over twenty feet, there was a difference of five feet in the level of the water above and below the bridge on the ebb tide, and as travelling by boat was the favorite mode of conveyance of the people of London at that time, " shooting the bridge " was an everyday experience. Pepys related in his diary how he was obliged to leave his boat and go around the bridge by land because his companion could not be persuaded to run the risk.

For the smaller streams wooden girder bridges, frequently on stone piers, were generally used. The shallower streams were crossed by fords, which were sometimes paved with stone. The remains of an old paved ford were removed from the river Trent near Lincoln in 1820.

The military engineers were skilful in constructing pile bridges. Julius Caesar is said to have built a pile bridge across the Saône in one day. The bridge across the Rhine, which he describes so minutely in his *Commentaries*, consisted of fifty-six bents of piles, spaced about twenty-five feet apart, each bent protected by a pile fender. The total length of the bridge was about fourteen hundred feet, and it was erected in ten days after the assembling of the material. Some pieces of piling have been found, which are thought to have been a part of this bridge.

The most remarkable of all the bridges of the Romans was the wooden arched bridge built by Trajan over the Danube in A.D. 106 Cassius Dio calls it a stone bridge and says it had twenty piers, one hundred and fifty feet high, and one hundred and seventy feet apart; Cassius Dio wrote long after the bridge had been taken down and he saw only the piers. The detailed construction of the bridge and the framing of the timbers are not known, but a representation of it is found among the bas reliefs on the column of Trajan; the sculpture represents a timber arch, somewhat like the arching in the Burr bridges so common in the last century. As Apollodorus of Damascus, the architect who erected the column, is believed to have been the engineer of the bridge, the bas relief is considered to be a correct representation, though deficient in detail, of the general type of the construction of the bridge. The arched members were composed of three parallel courses of timber, tied by braces or struts, which were continued upwards to the floor of the bridge and served as its support.

The abutting ends of the arch timbers appear
to have been quite insufficiently secured, and
no provision seems to have been made to prevent the buckling of the long timbers; this with
the absence of any counter bracing or of a stiff-
ening truss, must, with spans of such length,
have materially contributed to the short life
of the bridge.[19]

Thirty years after its construction it was taken
down by Hadrian's orders, as no longer needed
for the defence of the province of Moesia, but
the piers were left standing. This action has
been attributed to Hadrian's jealousy of Trajan,
but it is quite likely that the bridge had become
unsafe, and that the Emperor was unwilling to
authorize the expense of rebuilding. Much as
the detail of this bridge may be criticized, it
was a wonderful structure for its time, and
may be considered as a prototype of one of the
most popular forms of bridge construction of
the early nineteenth century; to quote Bergier:
"It showed the greatness of invincible cour-
age." The piers of this bridge rested on
foundations made by sinking barges loaded
with concrete, also rudely foreshadowing the
modern caisson.

Many important bridges were built in Italy.

One of the most perfectly preserved is the bridge at Rimini, carrying the *Via Flaminia* over the Marecchia River. Architecturally it is one of the most ornate of all the Roman bridges and was especially admired by Palladio. It was constructed during the reign of Augustus, about A.D. 20, and consisted of five arches, the three central arches having an opening of nearly twenty-nine feet, the two others having each an opening of about twenty-three and a half feet. The roadway is horizontal over the three central arches, nearly fifty feet above the bed of the river. Over each of the four piers, the spandrel is ornamented by a niche containing a statue, above which is a cornice surmounted by a marble parapet.

Near Narnia on the Flaminian Way are the ruins of an old bridge over the river Nar. It had four high arches of unequal span, the crowns being kept on the same level with the imposts at different heights. The greatest span was about 139 feet and the total length of the bridge about 626 feet. The roadway is 146 feet above the river.

The *Pons Salarius*, at the point where the *Via Salaria* crosses the river Anio, was constructed at the beginning of the fourth century.

It had one central arch of $87\frac{1}{2}$ feet span; the arch is set back on the imposts about six feet, perhaps to support the centering; the abutment walls are each pierced by an arch of about thirteen feet opening; a great part of the bridge is now covered by the alluvial deposits of the river.

Many of the most important of the Roman bridges are found in Spain, the most notable of all being the great bridge at Alcantara over the river Tagus on the road from Alcantara to Merida, constructed by Trajan about A.D. 109. The bridge has six arches of cut stone of very large size with accurately dressed joints, built without cement, the stones joined with iron cramps sealed with lead. The two middle arches have spans of $111\frac{1}{2}$ and 118 feet. The lateral arches have spans of about half that length. The total length of the bridge is over six hundred feet and its height above the water is about one hundred and seventy-five feet. An arch spans the roadway at the center of the bridge, bearing an inscription in honor of Trajan and naming C. Julius Lacer as the builder of the bridge. The piers, as was customary in Roman river bridges, have an acute angled cutwater at the upper end.

The bridge at Merida, over the river Guadiana, has sixty arches over thirty feet high with a total length of over 2500 feet. Over each of the piers the spandrel is pierced by a narrow arch, presumably to afford additional water way, as was often done in Roman bridges. The date of this bridge is disputed, but it is generally attributed to Trajan.

There were two bridges over the river Tormes, one at Salamanca of twenty-seven arches of sixty-six and a half feet opening and nearly one hundred and sixty feet above the river. The other near Ledesma was a bridge of five arches about sixty-five feet high at the keystones. The three middle arches are pointed, perhaps indicating a restoration by the Moors.

The Flavian bridge at St. Chamas over the river Touloubre in Gaul is notable for the ornamental pillared porticoes, one at each end of the bridge. The bridge consists of a single full-centered arch of thirty-three feet span; the abutments rest directly on the rock. This bridge is well preserved.

In the valley of Aosta on the road from Milan to Aosta and the Great and Little St. Bernard is the bridge of St. Martin over the

mountain torrent now called the Lys. This
bridge is well preserved, but it is not now in
use as the modern road crosses the stream at a
different point. It consists of a single arch
of one hundred and five feet span, about
seventy-five feet above the stream; the roadway has the somewhat unusual width of seventeen feet; the abutments rest on the solid rock.
A peculiar feature of this bridge is the construction of the vault which is built in parallel
rings of stone masonry, built independently and
some distance apart, with four intermediate
rings of concrete. The same method of construction was followed in another bridge a short
distance below, which was also built in nine
parallel rings, of which but one remains.

Not far from Aosta is a bridge called the
Pont d'El or Pondel crossing a narrow rocky
gorge about fifty feet wide. The bridge is a
single arch, the abutments are founded on the
solid rock over one hundred and thirty feet
above the bottom of the gorge. As the banks
of the gorge are about fifty feet higher than
the arch, the spandrel walls are carried up,
forming at the top a narrow gallery with a pas-
sageway about three and a half feet wide, the
width of the bridge itself, including the side

walls of the gallery, being only seven and a half feet. The gallery was provided with windows and had an arched opening in the lower side at each end of the bridge, and was probably intended to protect the passengers from the fierce mountain gales that blew down the gorge. An inscription on the bridge gives the date of its construction in the year 3 B.C.

At El-Kantara in Algeria is a single-arched bridge of about thirty-three feet span, sixteen feet wide and forty-seven feet high; it was constructed by the engineers of the Third Legion; the vault exhibited the same method of construction as the bridge of St. Martin, being built with three double arches, and the intermediate space filled with concrete.

Leger describes over fifty bridges in the various provinces of Rome.

It might be well to quote from Vitruvius (Bk. V, c. 12, on " Harbors and Breakwaters ") and learn what he says of coffer-dams:

" Then, in the place previously determined, a cofferdam, with its sides formed of oaken stakes with ties between them, is to be driven down into the water and firmly propped there; then, the lower surface, inside, under the water, must be levelled off and dredged, working from beams laid across; and finally, concrete from the mortar trough — the stuff having been mixed as prescribed above — must be heaped up until the empty space which was within the cofferdam is filled up by the wall."

"A cofferdam with double sides, composed of charred stakes fastened together with ties, should be constructed in the appointed place, and clay in wicker baskets made of swamp rushes should be packed in among the props. After this has been well packed down and filled in as closely as possible, set up your water-screws, wheels, and drums, and let the space now bounded by the enclosure be emptied and dried. Then dig out the bottom within the enclosure."

(c. 12, §§ 3 and 5, translation of
M. H. Morgan)

As Sig. Giovannoni says: "Modern technique, therefore, has inherited everything from the Romans in this most important branch (i.e. of bridge building), as well as in the parallel branch of harbour-construction. It has then added to these systems new mechanical developments for the drainage of water by means of pumps,[20] for excavation by dredges, and, finally, for sinking caissons by compressed air; but it has followed the same principles as were used experimentally in the great and lasting works of the Romans."

(Bailey, *The Legacy of Rome*, p. 463.)

With their limited facilities for rock excavation, without explosives, and without adequate tools, the Romans avoided the construction of tunnels; with the exception of the tunnels on the lines of the aqueducts and the drainage tunnels, but few important tunnels have been found. There was a tunnel between Puteoli and Naples about twenty-three hundred feet long and nineteen and a half feet wide, considerably enlarged at the ends, and a tunnel on the Flaminian Way built under Vespasian, nine hundred and eighty feet long. The half tunnel cut in the side of the rock near the Iron Gate of the Danube, for Trajan's road, might be included in the list of tunnels, but it is more properly a side-hill cutting.

VIII. TOWN–PLANNING, WALLS, AND *LIMITES*

ANCIENT towns, like many modern ones, usually grew and expanded without following any definite plan; although some evidence of a primitive and partial approximation to a regular plan has been observed in the ruins of some very ancient towns, most of the cities of Greece and Italy, including Rome, were laid out on very irregular lines. Yet, in Greece, the art of town-planning seems to have begun in Athens, in the fifth century B.C., when the architect, Hippodamus,[20a] of Miletus, is credited with planning straight wide streets at right angles in the Piraeus. In the latter part of the same century, Solinus seems to have adopted a definite building-plan and road-plan for that city. This included two main thoroughfares from end to end, crossing at right angles. The same scheme also existed in Cyrene, though we do not know the date of this. The first instance of city planning of any considerable scale occurred after

[170]

the conquest of western Asia by Alexander the Great, when there was a large immigration from Greece and Macedonia as well as a great number of the disbanded troops of his army who had to be provided with dwellings. Many cities were thus founded for their accommodation and the system of rectangular streets was adopted in nearly all cases. Turkey, in Asia, had many such cities, laid out with the regular chess-board plan for streets; Priene furnishes us an excellent illustration, and Miletus and Alexandria give testimony to the same effect; Nicaea in Bithynia presented the same rectangular effect. Pergamum, under the Attalid Kings, in the third and second centuries B.C., carried out a magnificent plan of a semi-circle of great buildings, adorning the crest and slopes of its crescent-shaped ridge. The Macedonian plan of square towns and parallel streets was fully established in the second century before Christ and was very similar to the arrangements of a Roman camp. In Italy, the early traces of a similar plan in the prehistoric Terramara of Castellazzo di Fontanellato are very striking. " Roma Quadrata " may refer to an ancient city, more or less rectangular in shape, on the Palatine. At a much later date, we find the rectangular plan, with streets running north and south, east and west, and crossing at right angles, employed by the *Coloniae*, which the Roman government established at various points throughout the empire. Piacenza, Bologna, Parma, Modena, Turin, Verona, Florence, and Lucca, for example, all furnish evidence of this principle, — Mediolanum (Milan) to a lesser extent.

With the Romans the founding of a city was a religious act and performed with well-defined ceremony.[21] The *Augur* took his position in the centre of the proposed site, and with this point as the intersection laid out the two principal streets of the new city, the *kardo* (*maximus*), running north and south, and the *decumanus* (*maximus*), running east and west; the width of the *kardo* was usually twenty feet, and of the *decumanus,* forty feet. Then a set of secondary streets was laid out with the *groma,* parallel to the main streets; those parallel to the *kardo maximus* were called *kardines* and those parallel to the *decumanus maximus* were called *decumani,* each being distinguished from the others by its ordinal number. The *kardo* and the *decumanus* divided the city plot into four regions. The *augur* facing the east, the *kardo* divided the *regio antica* in front of him from the *regio postica* behind him, and the *decumanus* separated the *regio sinistra* on his left hand from the *regio dextrata* on his right; so that by naming the region and the number belonging to any *kardo* or *decumanus,* any point in the city could be designated. The central point, where the *kardo* and the *decumanus* intersected, was the proper place for the forum and other public buildings. In many cities laid out in this way the old street plan has been preserved; though buried in most cases beneath modern constructions, the plan can be recovered by excavations. At Turin, which was founded as a *colonia* by Augustus, 28 B.C., the old street plan has been almost entirely preserved, and the greater part of modern Turin has been laid out in continuation of the original lines laid out by the Romans. The Via Garibaldi represents the old Roman *decumanus maximus.* At Aosta, which was also an Augustan colony, the old Roman streets are from eight to ten feet below the present street level, but the modern street lines follow with some irregularity the lines of the ancient streets. About five feet below the old pavement are the old sewers, for the Romans always constructed sewers when they laid out a town. These sewers in Aosta had so long gone out of use that in the middle ages the inhabitants, who had only surface drainage, supposed that the sewers were tunnels intended as a means of escape if the city were captured by assault.

In the provinces, also, we find relics of ancient town-planning and of the chess-board pattern of intersecting streets: two or three streets in Cologne; Timgad in Roman Africa, in Numidia, that brilliant colony of Trajan; Orange has yielded an inscription telling of a plot, fronting AD K, or *on the kardo*. Carthage, and Lincoln in England, should be mentioned; others are discussed by Haverfield.

Many modern cities have followed the street plan of the Roman cities. Professor Haverfield mentions Philadelphia as a prominent example, and the division of the city into four regions and numbering the streets in both directions from the central point is a distinctive feature of the city of Washington.

A precisely similar system was employed in dividing lands, as in those granted to colonists.

Decimanus appellatur limes, qui fit ab ortu solis ad occasum; alter ex transverso currens appellatur cardo.

The boundary-line that leads from the setting of the sun to its rising, is called the *decumanus;* the other, crossing it at right angles, is called the *cardo*. (Pauli-Fest., 71M = p. 62, Lindsay)

Qui ita limes per agrum currit *cardo* appellatur, i.e. N. to S. (Pliny, *N.H.*, XVIII. 33. 76. 326.)

The surveyor set up his *groma* at the center of the plot to be divided and traced on the ground the lines of the *decumanus* and *kardo*. The lots were then marked by a series of *decumani* and *kardines* parallel to the first. The unit of land measure was ordinarily a square of 240 feet; one hundred of these made a *centuria,* which was a square of 2400 feet on the side. Roads were established on the lines of the *kardo* (*maximus*) and the *decumanus* (*maximus*), and smaller roads on the line of every fifth of the others. Boundary stones were set at the corners. Some of these have been found, and in several parts of Italy traces of the ancient " centuriation " are still discernible.

No ancient city was complete without its wall. In his first book Vitruvius treats of proper sites for cities, and (Ch. 5) of city walls,

[175]

describing in some detail how they should be located, and built, with projecting towers and internal galleries for the movement of the soldiers of the garrison. Professor Burr, in his *Ancient and Modern Engineering*, writes that " in no class of engineering work did the Romans display greater skill than in the massive walls of cut stone with which they surrounded their city."

The Palatine Hill was protected by a wall that came to be called the *murus Romuli*. Of this wall, one fragment, still standing at the southwest angle of the hill, was built of gray-green tufa (*cappellacio*); it may be as early as the sixth century B.C., since its masonry corresponds closely to that of the foundations of the temple of Jupiter on the Capitoline hill; another fragment, of friable brown tufa blocks, laid in alternate courses of headers and stretchers, belongs, apparently, to a rebuilding of later date, perhaps early in the fifth century; its blocks bear masons' marks and its workmanship is superior to that of the earlier fragment. This wall probably followed the line of a much earlier wall, of which no traces remain. Its stones are not carelessly cut polygonal blocks, but, on the contrary, the wall was built of squared stone, two feet thick, laid in alternate courses of headers and stretchers. The stones were quarry-faced, with beds and joints carefully dressed. The stone used was a soft tufa, readily worked with primitive tools, and immediately available in large quantities. On the hillside, the wall was set about forty feet below the summit. It was about ten feet thick at the base, and about forty feet in height.

Of its gates, the *porta Mugonia,* or cattle-gate is the most famous.

As the city grew, another wall was built, generally ascribed to Servius Tullius, and consequently known as the " Servian Wall."

But the existing fragments of this wall are not of the original construction. They resemble, rather, the fragment of the " Wall of Romulus " which has been dated as of the fifth century, and may represent a reconstruction, following, perhaps, the destruction of the city by the Gauls in 390 B.C. (the fourth century), The wall was built on a shelf, cut in the slope of the hills, as was the Palatine Wall. The blocks of tufa were laid in alternate courses of headers and stretchers, without mortar. The blocks were carefully cut, the edges carefully worked, and were very regular. One great fragment on the Aventine was built of brown tufa and another fragment on the northwest slope of the Quirinal, of gray-green tufa blocks. Across the tableland of the Esquiline, between the *porta Collina* and the *porta Esquilina,* was the famous *agger,* a combination of trench, embankment and wall. Of the wall of this *agger,* as is well known, a large portion remains. A trench was dug, the earth thrown toward the inside making an embankment; this embankment was supported by one wall on the outside, opus quadratum, of brown tufa, from the bottom of the trench to the top of the embankment; a second wall of gray-green tufa, built on the inside. The whole has been described by Dionysius of Halicarnassus (IX. 68). Livy refers briefly to the fortifications of Servius Tullius in these words:

Aggere et fossis et muro circumdat urbem. (I. 44)

Whether the city was defended by a wall, along the river front, is not known for a surety, but it is generally thought not. There are many allusions in the literature to the gates of this wall, the most famous of which was the *porta Capena,* through which the Via Appia led, to the south. The construction of this wall resembles that of the fragments of the wall of Romulus, but at several points it may have been provided with counterforts, nine feet wide, and projecting seven or eight feet from the wall. The greater part of the Servian wall has been destroyed but its entire course has been traced, with great exactness, with the help of literary references and inscriptions. Its total length was 5⅜ Roman miles.

A third wall was commenced in A.D. 271 by the Emperor Aurelian and completed by Probus in 280; it was partly destroyed by Alaric and rebuilt by Honorius in 402; on the east side of the Tiber, the wall is built of brick-faced concrete about twelve feet thick, and it was 8 to 16 metres high, varying, according to topographical conditions. It had an internal gallery about ten feet above the ground, and at intervals of ninety to one hundred feet, more than three hundred square towers were built with rooms for soldiers; the walls of the towers were pierced with embrasures for the discharge of missiles; the towers projected from twelve to fifteen feet from the face of the wall, commanding the interval on each side.

Of its gates, the most famous are:

The *porta Flaminia,* through which the Flaminian road ran (porta del Popolo);

The *porta Tiburtina,* under which passed the *via Tiburtina* and the *via Collatina* (porta S. Lorenzo);

The *porta Praenestina,* exit of the *via Praenestina* (porta Maggiore);

The *porta Appia,* through which ran the Appian Way (porta S. Sebastiano);

The *porta Ostensiensis,* with its road to Ostia, and hard by, the tomb of Cestius (porta S. Paolo);

The *porta Aurelia,* on the Janiculan Hill, exit for the Aurelian Way (porta S. Pancrazio).

With the weak artillery of those days, a wall was a strong defence, and not only the cities but the boundaries of the Empire were thus fortified. In Britain the northern frontier was defended by two walls. The upper wall, extending from the Forth to the Clyde, called the wall of Antoninus, now known locally as "Graham's Dyke," was composed chiefly of earth confined between stone curbs. It is of little historical importance, but it is said to have been constructed with considerable engineering skill, taking the high ground and commanding, throughout most of its course, the lower ground in front. The lower wall was constructed by Hadrian and afterwards repaired. It extended from a point on the Tyne, still known as Wallsend, to Bowness on the Solway, a distance of eighty Roman or about seventy-three and a half English miles. Hadrian's wall has been called the greatest monument of Roman power in England.[22]

Hadrian's wall was built of masonry throughout, from six to ten feet thick, and was probably eighteen or nineteen feet high when built; in front of the wall was a trench thirty-six feet wide and fifteen feet deep. In the rear was a military road, and south of the road a rampart and trench, known as *Vallum*, which has been the subject of much discussion by the English archaeologists. The wall and *vallum* are generally close together, but are occasionally a half mile or more apart, no doubt for military or topographical reasons; the *vallum* being more direct, while the wall occupies the military crest on the northern slopes and often makes a detour to avoid low ground. At intervals along the wall are the ruins of nineteen garrison stations or forts, and at distances of a mile apart were *castella* fifty feet square, with gates opening north and south.

Except where stone had been taken from the wall to build houses in the vicinity, Hadrian's wall remained in a substantial state of preservation until 1745, when great quantities of stone were taken for the construction of the road built by General Wade from Newcastle to Carlisle; Stukeley, writing in 1754, is indignant at the quantity of cut stone ashlars that had been taken from the wall and broken up for road metal when other suitable stone might have been procured in the neighborhood, and also because in his opinion the old Roman road should have been used instead of making a new one.

Less strongly fortified than the wall of Hadrian was the line of forts that marked the *limes* or boundary of the Empire from the Rhine to the Danube.[23] The word *limes* denoted a road or cross-path separating two fields, and thence it derived the secondary meaning of an artificial boundary-line between fields or estates; it gained the meaning of a fortified boundary-line, or a boundary-wall, and of a frontier; but not, generally, in the sense of a precise or definite line of demarcation. It signified the military line of defensive frontier fortifications rather than the actual limit of

Roman occupation. In this sense the wall of Hadrian was a *limes,* although the Romans maintained fortified stations and permanent garrisons north of the wall, as they also did in the Dobrudja. The road was protected throughout by a stockade of heavy oak timbers, nine feet high; traces of this stockade have been found all along the line. In the eastern section of the Raetian frontier the stockade was replaced by a massive stone wall, of smaller dimensions than Hadrian's wall, but much longer, being over one hundred miles long, and nearly eight feet high; on the eastern Danube section there was another wall over thirty-seven miles long with a trench thirty feet wide and nearly ten feet deep. The object of the *limes* was not so much to interpose a continuous line of defence as to provide for quick communication with the garrisons held in reserve, either in *castella* on the line of the *limes,* or in forts advantageously located in the rear, and to make possible the rapid movement of reinforcements to the point of attack, the stockade or wall presenting a defensible impediment to the advance of the invaders, where they might be held in check until the reinforcements arrived. Ready communication between the watch towers on the line and the supporting forts was probably had by means of fire and smoke signals; Mr. Macdonald presents evidence to show that regular provision was made in the construction of the forts on the wall of Antoninus for firing large heaps of wood, kept in readiness for instant use in making signals, and certain of the sculptures on the column of Trajan are supposed to represent signal stations of this sort.

IX. CLOACAE, CANALS, RECLAMATIONS, AND HARBORS

THE CITY of Rome is built on a group of hills, whose summits are from one hundred and fifty to about two hundred and fifty feet above the sea, the low ground between the hills being originally a continuous swamp, fed by numerous springs and intersected by several streams. While still under the kings, the Romans began the construction of the *cloacae,* or sewers, on the lines of these streams.

The first of these *cloacae* was the Cloaca Maxima,[24] supposed to date from the time of Tarquinius Superbus; Livy speaks of its construction in these words:

et infima urbis loca circa forum aliasque interiectas collibus convalles, quia ex planis locis haud facile evehebant aquas, cloacis fastigio in Tiberim ductis siccat, (Liv., I. 38. 6)

" and he (Tarquinius Priscus) drained the lowest parts of the city, about the Forum, and the other valleys, between the hills, which were too flat to

carry off the flood-waters, easily, by means of
sewers so made as to slope down toward the Tiber."
(Tr. of Foster, in *The Loeb Classical Library*),

Cloacamque maximam, receptaculum omnium
purgamentorum urbis, sub terra agendam; quibus
duobus operibus vix nova haec magnificentia quic-
quam adaequare potuit. (Liv., I. 56. 2, time of
Tarquinius Superbus)

" I mean the erection in the circus, and the construction underground of the Great Sewer, as a
receptacle for all the offscourings of the City, —
two works for which the new splendors of these
days has scarcely been able to produce a match."
(Foster).

The oldest part of the existing structure is
probably not older than the third century B.C.,
and much of it consists of restorations made
during the Empire, the roof in some places being made of concrete. It is very crooked, no
doubt following the line of the original stream.
The other streams of Rome were converted
into similar *cloacae,* and in time there was a
network of these drains under the city, so
that Pliny, speaking of the *urbis nostrae
miracula,* said:

tum . . . mirabantur praeterea cloacas, opus omnium dictu maximum, subfossis montibus atque

. . . urbe pensili supterque navigata. (*N. H.,*
XXXVI, 15. 24. 104)

then they marvelled also at the *cloacae,* the greatest work of all, which required digging under mountains, and the city hung in space over the drains
navigated below.

Remains of the drains have been found in
many places and in a few instances the old
sewers are actually still in use.

The arch of the Cloaca Maxima, where it
debouches into the Tiber, is semicircular, between eleven and twelve feet in diameter, the
crown of the arch being about twelve feet
above the pavement. At the present time the
ordinary level of the water in the river is very
nearly at the same elevation as the springing
line of the arch. The old accounts speak of the
Cloaca as navigable by small boats, though
this is now impossible. This indicates that the
level of the surface of the water has risen considerably since the construction of the Cloaca,
and similarly the excavations made by Lanciani
show that the present level of the ground water
is much higher than of old. This rise in the
level of the water may be readily accounted
for by the greater distance from Rome to the
sea, today, as the shore line has been con-

tinuously moving seaward since Rome's earliest days. How many feet the water has risen is indeterminate. Surveys made by the distinguished astronomer and physicist, Father Secchi, S. J., and by the engineers of the embankment, indicate that the bed of the stream has risen less than three feet, which seems insufficient to account for the conditions at the mouth of the Cloaca. The rise in elevation of the surface of the water and of the bed of the river are not necessarily identical, and the discrepancy may be thus accounted for. There does not appear to have been any subsidence of the land, such as occurred at Pozzuoli, or at the bay of Baiae, near Naples.[25]

Large openings were made in the streets for the admission of surface and storm water into the cloacae; these openings were provided with covers, often of ornamental design.

In the narrow and crowded streets of Rome, these sewer openings were a constant source of danger, as may well be imagined. Suetonius (*De. Gram.*, 2), who was fond of anecdote, tells us that Crates of Mallos, while resident in Rome, as the delegate of King Attalus of Pergamum, fell into one of them in the Palatine region, and broke his leg. Notwithstanding the accident, Crates, who was also a lecturer on grammar, continued his lectures during the entire period of his convalescence; thus, as Suetonius quaintly observes, setting " an example to be imitated by the Roman litterateurs."

While the Roman sewers did not comply with the requirements of modern hygienic engineering they were quite as good as those of any city of modern Europe, until very recent times. Of their structural merit, Lanciani writes: " there is no doubt that the work is simply wonderful. An immense sewer built twenty-five centuries ago, on unstable ground, under enormous practical difficulties, which still answers its purpose, is a work to be classed among the greatest triumphs of engineering."

One of the most notable works of the Romans was the drainage canal, constructed by Claudius in A.D. 52, to carry off the water of Lake Fucinus, to the river Liris, now called the Garigliano, by a tunnel through Mt. Salviano.[26] The lake occupied a depression in the mountain and having no outlet was subject to great variations in the height of the water; in rainy seasons it was a menace to the surrounding territory, and in dry weather the fertile plains which it had submerged became an offensive marsh. The tunnel was three and a half miles long with a cross-sectional of about sixteen square yards, affording much better opportunity for the removal of the excavated material than the narrow tunnel of Mt. Affliano. The work was greatly facilitated by numerous shafts sunk along the line, permitting the work to be carried on simultaneously at several different places. Suetonius relates that thirty thousand men were continuously employed on this work for eleven years. Soon after its completion it became obstructed; the lake is now drained by a new tunnel, completed in 1876, which follows closely the location of the old one.

A similar project, although executed very much earlier, was the drainage tunnel of Lake Albano, constructed soon after the taking of Veii, some time between 396 and 350 B.C. Lake Albano, like Lake Fucinus, filled the crater of an extinct volcano and was without outlet. The tunnel was about a mile and a third long, with cross-section about six feet in height and between three and a half and four feet wide, and it had air-shafts at intervals of about 35 metres. From the outlet of the tunnel the water is conveyed about fifteen miles in an open channel to the Tiber. This tunnel is still in use and the water from the lake is used for irrigation.

A work of similar character is the drainage of the plain of Reate by the construction of a canal, in the third century before Christ, to carry off the waters of the Veline lake; the canal was a little over a half mile long, partly in rock cutting.

The Emperor Nero undertook the construction of a ship canal from Ostia to Lake Avernus near the Bay of Naples, but abandoned the work before completion. It included a tunnel on the north side of the lake, which was discovered in 1507. The length of the proposed canal was one hundred and sixty Roman miles and its breadth sufficient to allow ships of five banks of oars to pass each other. The engineers of this work were Severus and Celer who were also Nero's engineers for the rebuilding of Rome after the great fire. The plans for the rebuilding are said to have been drawn before the fire.

Before Nero's time, however, there was a canal in operation between Tarracina and Forum Appii, and Strabo (V. 3. 6. C. 233) tells us that it was customary for travellers to take passage on the canal boats by night, embarking at Tarracina in the evening, disembarking in the morning, and going the rest of the way to Rome by the Via Appia. This implies a line of stage coaches on the Appian Way, and sleeping accommodations on the boats, indicating that the facilities for travel in the Augustan age were comparable to those in use among ourselves a hundred years ago. In a famous satire Horace has given us a vivid description of the doubtful pleasures of a night ride on this canal.[27]

Canals, perhaps intended primarily for the purpose of providing additional outlets for floods, but available for navigation, were constructed by Drusus, while in command of the Roman army, between the Rhine and the Ysel, and by Claudius between the Rhine and the Meuse.

The Tiber is subject to great floods; the greatest was in 1598, when the water rose forty-two feet; in this flood fifteen hundred people were drowned and two arches of the Pons Aemilius overthrown. The Romans began, very early in their history, the construction of river walls to control the floods; the wall at the mouth of the Cloaca Maxima is supposed to antedate the second century B.C. During the empire, embankment walls were built on both sides of the river; in order to adjust the width of the channel to the varying size of the river, the ancient engineers built their embankment in three stages, stepping back at each stage, so that the width of the waterway was $62\frac{1}{2}$ metres at the lowest stage, $97\frac{1}{2}$ at the intermediate stage, and 135 metres at the top. After the flood of 1870, the Italian government built embankments at the uniform width apart of 100 metres. Here the old engineering was better than the new, the excessive width of the new channel, only partly occupied by the stream, being very objectionable at low water.[28]

In England besides the construction of river walls and embankments on the Thames, the Romans undertook the great work of the reclamation of the country of the Fens on the borders of the Wash, the great estuary that separates Lincolnshire from Norfolk. The Fen country extends southward nearly to Cambridge, and is bounded by the higher ground of six counties, comprising an area of about four hundred square miles; its length being about sixty miles and its greatest breadth twenty miles. Near the sea, the country is a salt marsh seven miles wide on both shores of the Wash and extending north to the Humber; inland is the low flat land of the Fens, slightly elevated above the water of the rivers and flooded by every freshet in the sluggish streams that wind their uncertain way to the sea; Hilaire Belloc describes it as the country where no one can tell where the land ends or the sea begins; this country is now one of the most fertile districts of England.

The Romans built an intercepting canal, known as the Carr-Dyke, about sixty feet wide and forty miles long, from Peterborough on the Nene to the Witham, three miles below Lincoln. Of the Carr-Dyke, Rennie, one of England's early engineers, who was in charge of the reclamation of the Fens in 1818, said: " I have traced its course for the greater part of the way and a more judicious and well laid out work I have never seen."

A mile above Lincoln, a continuation of the Carr-Dyke, known as the Fosse-Dyke, connected the Witham with the Trent, thus affording a continuous navigable waterway from Peterborough to the Humber, and thence by way of the Ouse to York, giving direct water communication to ten of the present counties.

In connection with these drainage canals, the

Romans built a causeway or levee along the shore, sixty feet wide and thirty miles long, for the protection of the low lands, and it also served as a military road. A portion of this causeway is still visible, and the Carr-Dyke can be traced almost all the way from Peterborough to Lincoln.

It was while crossing the Nene near the point where it empties into the Wash, that King John's army was caught by the bore of the incoming flood tide; Falconbridge tells the story:

" I *tell thee Hubert, half my power this night,*
Passing the flats, are taken by the tide;
These Lincoln Washes have devoured them.
Myself well mounted, barely have escaped."
(*King John,* Act V, Sc. VI and VII).

Rennie attributes great injury to the country from the neglect to keep the Roman works in repair; perhaps if the Roman engineers had remained in England those eight hundred years, there might have been a safe crossing for King John's army.

After the departure of the Romans, little attention seems to have been given to the maintenance of the Roman works until the establishment of the Benedictine monasteries at Ely, Peterborough and Croyland, where there were little patches or islands of higher ground. Manual labor was always an important part of the Benedictine discipline, and the reclamation of waste land was a favorite enterprise with them, as it had been in various parts of Europe; and they were no doubt familiar with similar works in Italy and elsewhere. After the suppression of the Monasteries by Henry VIII, the work was taken over by the government, but little was done until the reign of Charles I, when a new embankment was built by Vermuyden, the Dutch engineer, who had been brought to England to repair the broken embankments on the Thames. The work was finally completed in the early part of the nineteenth century by the English engineers, Rennie and Telford.

As Rome depended on foreign importations for its support, its commerce was large. The arrival of the fleet of grain ships from Alexandria was the great commercial event of the year. Lookouts were established on the heights of Misenum, on the coast, west of Puteoli, to watch for the expected fleet, and information of its arrival was immediately signaled to Rome.

It was on two of these grain ships that St. Paul took passage on his way to Rome, the first going ashore at Malta; the second, probably too large to dock at Ostia, landed at Puteoli, from which place the Apostle proceeded, arriving at Rome by the Appian Way.

On account of the increasing shallowness of the harbor of Ostia,[29] and the difficult navigation to the sea, the Emperor Claudius constructed an artificial harbor, protected by jetties and a breakwater, two miles up the coast; it covered an area of one hundred and forty acres, and the quays were a mile and a half long. The breakwater was built on the line of the jetties, leaving the openings unprotected from the sea; this fault in the design was the cause of the destruction of two hundred vessels in one storm. The breakwater was constructed by taking the ship that had brought the Vatican obelisk from Egypt, a large ship that carried a cargo of one thousand tons of lentils besides the obelisk, sinking it, filled with concrete, on the line of the breakwater, and completing the work by a riprap of large stones. The completed breakwater was crowned by a lighthouse two hundred feet high. The harbor of Claudius was connected with the Tiber by a

canal which has since become the principal
channel of the river.

The facilities afforded by the harbor of
Claudius becoming insufficient for the increasing commerce of the city, the Emperor Trajan
constructed another between it and the Tiber;
it was hexagonal in shape, and covered an area
of ninety acres, with quay walls nearly a mile
and a quarter long, with eighteen feet depth
of water. Trajan's harbor, now two miles from
the sea, is now called the Lago Trajano, and
the ruins of its warehouses illustrate, by their
marble columns, mosaic pavements, and sculp-
tured moorings, the magnificence with which
the Romans used to decorate their most practical designs. Other important harbors were
protected by moles; at Tarracina the mole was
two thousand feet long, with an opening over
three hundred feet wide for the passage of vessels; this opening was on the eastern side of the
harbor for better protection from the sea. Leger
states that the harbor of Fréjus was large
enough to contain three hundred vessels which
Augustus had taken from Antony at the battle
of Actium.

Nearly all the Roman harbors had lighthouses; the ruins of some of them exist, others

have been entirely lost. Many of them were built in imitation of the Pharos of Alexandria, commenced during the reign of Ptolemy Soter, 299 B.C., and completed, 284 B.C., by his successor, Ptolemy Philadelphus. It was built of heavy stone bedded in sheets of lead or bonded by gudgeons or dowels made fast by lead, and faced with marble; its height is not certainly known but it may have been three or four hundred feet high. It was overthrown by an earthquake in 1303.

The lighthouse at Ostia was built in seven stories on a square base about one hundred and ninety feet on the side. The lighthouse of Fréjus, of which a part remains between seventy-five and seventy-eight feet in height, was circular with a diameter of about thirty-five feet; at this lighthouse were found storerooms for the storage of the wood used for producing the light. The principal lighthouse in Gaul was at Boulogne; it was originally twelve stories high, each story forming a truncated octagonal pyramid, about sixty-five feet in diameter at the base. The cliff on which it was built yielded to the approach of the sea in 1644 and fell, carrying the tower with it. The tower at Dover was also octagonal; the interior, how-

ever, was square with vertical walls; near by
was found another tower square in section,
somewhat less than sixty feet in diameter, which
from the description by Leger, seems to have
been intended for a signal tower or marker for
the guidance of vessels approaching from various directions. The lighting was probably in
all cases produced by wood fires kept burning
on the top of the tower. After the Romans, no
lighthouses of importance were built until the
twelfth or thirteenth century.

The Romans appreciated the value of the
metals. Tacitus speaks of the mineral wealth
of Britain as the " prize of victory," and there
is little doubt that the possession of important
mining regions was a motive of conquest.
Within six years after the second invasion of
Britain, the Romans had begun the production
of lead, which Britain produced more abund-
antly than any other province. They developed
the tin mines of Cornwall, from which the
Phoenicians had previously obtained their supply; and copper was mined in Cornwall and
Wales. The remains of iron mines and iron
forges have been found in many places in England, particularly in Sussex and Kent, where
there are immense banks of forge cinders

twenty feet high, and extending for miles. Coal mines were opened near Newcastle and in Lancashire, and coal was used for heating the hypocausts of Roman villas in districts where it was readily procured; and coal ashes have been found in the garrison stations of Hadrian's Wall.

Pliny [30] describes the gold mines of Spain, with galleries and tunnels, the roofs of which were supported by arches, where the miners worked by the light of torches and never saw the daylight for months at a time. He also describes bank-mining by undercutting the face of the bank of gold-bearing gravel, and washing the gravel by water brought from the mountains by flumes, where the engineers taking the levels and marking the courses of the flumes along the precipitous rocks were suspended by ropes and looked like birds in the air.

A recent writer [31] supplements Pliny's account by describing the method employed to get rid of the debris that accumulated in the river from the washings; great reservoirs were built and the entire contents discharged at once into the stream, carrying the deposits of stone and gravel into the sea. The same writer praises the accuracy of the ancient engineers in establishing the grades of the flumes, which had an average gradient of twelve feet per mile.

The study of Roman engineering is full of interest to the modern engineer; most of our knowledge of the subject is derived from the examination of the ruined remains of their great works, and of the few structures that have survived, for Roman writers have left us but scanty memorials of them; the ancient excellence in every department of engineering excites our admiration; as has been well remarked by Leger: "The Romans were the first of the nations of antiquity to cover the entire field of engineering works; others, the Assyrians, the Egyptians, the Phoenicians, the Carthaginians had before them directed their efforts to certain isolated branches of public utility; the Romans developed them all.[32] "

X. THE CONTINUANCE OF THE ROMAN TRADITION AFTER THE FALL OF THE EMPIRE

THE persistence of the Roman type of construction and the influence of the Roman tradition during the period of transition that followed the fall of the empire, until the beginning of the modern era, have been touched upon to some extent in the previous chapters, and but little more need be added to show how the new engineering was built upon the old; modified, indeed, but, still, a development of the old rather than the creation of a new art. The fall of the empire was a gradual decay rather than a sudden collapse; the local governments still continued to regard Rome as, at least, their nominal head, and in some of the provinces the old Roman spirit was better preserved than in Rome itself. It was in southern Gaul, Spain, and northern Italy, that the Roman tradition was the strongest, for there the people were the most thoroughly imbued with Roman culture, and there even their conquerors had, to a large extent, become Romanized themselves.

In all of these countries, the division into smaller states and the consequently increasing disorder were unfavorable to engineering progress; and with the exception of the aqueduct of Spoleto in Italy, thought by some to date from the seventh century, few works of importance were attempted. For a brief period during the time of Charlemagne, extensive repairs were made to the roads, but afterwards, even the repairs to existing works were generally neglected. During these unsettled times, the monasteries became the natural abode of the learning and the science of the time; and, particularly, in the Benedictine order, which was widely established in Italy, France, and England, the monks became the architects and engineers as well as the preservers of the literary relics of former times. From this beginning was developed the semi-religious order, known as the " Brothers of the Bridge," *Fratres Pontis,* or *Fratres Pontifices,* founded in France by St. Bénézet. Their principal field of operation was in the south of France; in Italy, similar work was undertaken by other orders; and in

England, besides the Brothers of the Bridge, by the diocesan bishops.[33] Many bridges were constructed in the twelfth century by the Brothers of the Bridge, although few had been built in the previous centuries from the ninth to the twelfth. They followed Roman models closely, using the full centered arch, the heavy piers of large cut stone, with narrow waterways.

But little progress was made in engineering until the fifteenth century, when the revival of industry and commerce that followed the close of the Hundred Years War, in 1453, marked the beginning of the period of transition that preceded the era of modern engineering.

During the reign of Louis XIV, Colbert began the construction of public roads and also built many bridges, still following Roman models, with wide piers and narrow waterways; in some of the bridges of this period, attempts were made to take advantage of the rush of water between the piers by setting up mills, as Belisarius had done at Rome in the Gothic war, and which was also done at the first London bridge; but this, of course, made matters worse, and many of these bridges were carried away by floods; the bridge at Blois having to be rebuilt four times in one century. The same adherence to the Roman type of construction was shown by the Italian engineers during the early Renaissance, and was defended by Palladio, who declared that they could not be inspired by better models. During this period some noteworthy improvements in the art of bridge-building were made, particularly the reduction in the rise of the arch by the use of segmental, and three centered, or " basket-handle " arches; and in the seventeenth and eighteenth centuries bridge-building was put upon a more scientific basis by the works of Vauban, Perronet, and others; Perronet's bridge at Neuilly, on the Seine, serving in turn as a study for Telford in England.[34]

The influence of the Roman tradition was strengthened by Poggio's discovery of the *De Architectura* of Vitruvius, which at once became the standard authority for the engineers and architects of Europe. Leonardo da Vinci, Michael Angelo, Palladio, and all the leading engineers of the times were students of Vitruvius; Leonardo learned Latin so that he might read it in the original; Raphael read it in Calvo's translation, a copy of which, with marginal notes in Raphael's own hand, has been found in the library of Munich. The influence of Vitruvius extended to England; Telford read Vitruvius in 1792; Newton, in the preface to his translation, states that he was impelled to the task in order that England might no longer be the only country that did not possess the writings of Vitruvius in its own language.

But besides the study of Vitruvius the Italian engineers and architects of the Renaissance devoted themselves to the study of the architectural and engineering works of Rome, and Vasari in his *Lives of the Painters* very directly intimates that Brunelleschi was inspired by his examination of the dome of the Pantheon to his design for the dome of S. Maria del Fiore in Florence.

In the revival of engineering, as in the revival of letters, Italy and France, the countries nearest to old Rome, took the lead; England, more remote, was the most backward, and for years was dependent upon foreign engineers. The first London bridge, begun in 1176, was completed in 1209, by the French engineer Isembert; and the second London bridge, at Westminster, was built in 1738–50 by Labelye, also a French engineer; and when Smeaton, one of England's earliest and greatest engineers, began his studies, he was obliged to learn the French language, because there were no books on engineering subjects in English.

In the earlier days of iron bridges, the European engineers showed a decided preference for the arched type of construction, much more in vogue in Europe than in America. Dr. Waddell attributes this preference, in great part, to the influence of the old masonry arch " on the minds of the European bridge designers "; Telford expresses the same thought, when he writes, in his account of the first iron bridge in England, that its designers had not " disengaged their minds from the masonry arch."

In the eighteenth century, with Smeaton, the first in England to assume the title of Civil Engineer, and his English and European contemporaries, modern engineering may be said to have begun, the new engineering being distinguished from the old by new sources of power, better mechanical devices, and the application of mathematical analysis; but, as has been remarked by Leger: " The new theories have most often but confirmed the old practice; we have improved the details, without changing the principles. The most notable improvement in our modern practice is in the larger application of metallic construction. Outside of these new solutions of old problems, the ancients have left us but little to improve, except in the material and in the process of our work-shops." [35]

But while it is from the Romans that we have derived the beginnings of our engineering, we must not forget our debt to the Greeks, who were in many ways the instructors of the Romans, and were associated with them as the professional practitioners of the art and as the engineers of many of their most impor-tant works; we cannot measure that debt ex-actly, but it was very great. The Romans developed a new engineering, but they were aware of their debt to Greece, in architecture as well as engineering. As for the architects, Trajan expressed himself very happily when he wrote to Pliny and said: " It is usually from Greece that they come hither." [36]

NOTES AND BIBLIOGRAPHY

NOTES

1. Strabo, IX. 2. 16–18; see article, "Prehistoric Engineering at Lake Copais," in *Popular Science Monthly*, Dec. 1895; and articles in *Engineering Magazine*, Feb. 1904; *Scientific American Supplement*, Aug. 21, 1886; *The Engineer*, July 9, 1886.

2. Germain de Montauzan, *La Science Rom.*, p. 50; *The Legacy of Rome*, p. 298; Jones, p. 16; De Tissot, p. 49; Schöne, in *Jahrbuch des Kais. Deut. Arch. Inst.*, vol. XIV, p. 91; F. Ferrero, *Valley of Aosta*, p. 196.

3. S. B. Platner, *The Topography and Monuments of Ancient Rome;* J. H. Middleton, *The Remains of Ancient Rome;* R. Lanciani, *The Ruins and Excavations of Ancient Rome;* H. Stuart Jones, *Classical Rome,* London and New York, 1910; Tenney Frank, *Roman Buildings of the Republic,* American Academy in Rome.

4. Vitruvius is here, as well as in I. 5. 3., speaking of two walls, inner and outer, that constitute the two faces of a wall. He recommends the use of ties of charred olivewood, or of iron cramps to bind the two faces together, to give the wall lasting endurance.

5. Leger, pp. 581, 612.

6. Frontinus, II. 112; Burr, p. 48; Herschel, pp. 204, 208; Lanciani, *Commentarii di Frontino*, p. 363.

7. Frontinus, 124; Herschel, 257.

8. Lanciani, *Destruction of Rome*, pp. 85, 240; *Ancient Rome*, p. 154.

9. Cagnat et Chapot, pp. 40–47; Jones, pp. 40–43; Leger, pp. 143–250; Platner, p. 124; Duruy, *History of Rome,* vol. I, p. 495; Mommsen, *History of Rome*, Bk. III, ch. VII; Niebuhr, *Lectures on Roman History,* vol. III, p. 22.

10. Burr, p. 2; Cagnat et Chapot, p. 42; Leger, pp. 157

[213]

seq; Bulletin No. 220, U. S. Dept. of Agriculture, *Road Models.*

11. Vitruvius, VII. 1., discusses " floors " and (§ 6) uses the words *statuminatio* (bed), *rudus,* and *nucleus,* upon which the floor (*pavimentum*) was laid. Pliny also discussed *pavimenta* (*Nat. Hist.,* XXXVI. 25. 60. 184-186).

12. Smiles, *Lives of the Engineers,* vol. II, p. 158, edition of 1862, vol. III, p. 4, edition of 1874.

13. Thomas Ashby, Jr., " The Classical Topography of the Roman Campagna," in *Papers of the British School at Rome,* vols. I. III. IV. V. (1904–1910). G. Tomassetti, *La Campagna Romana,* 3 vols., Rome, 1910–1913. Platner gives an admirable brief summary of the roads and indicates the survivals of ancient roads as modern highways, within the city walls. Cf. Ashby, *The Roman Campagna,* 1927.

14. For Alpine Roads, cf. Coolidge, pp. 150–198; Friedlaender, Appendix, note to vol. I, p. 193; Jones, pp. 43, 44; Lanciani, *Wanderings in the Roman Campagna,* pp. 30–33; Leger, pp. 163, 187, 193.

15. Dr. H. Meyer, in *Mittheilungen der Antiq. Gesellschaft,* vol. XIII, pp. 117–139; W. T. Arnold, " Roman Roads," in *Spectator,* Aug. 30, 1902.

16. *Purgatorio,* X. 73 *seq.* (Longfellow's trans.).

17. Giovannoni, in *Legacy of Rome,* 464.

18. For the bridges at Rome, cf. Platner; Lanciani, *Ruins and Excavations;* Middleton; Mayerhöfer, *Die Brücken im alten Rom;* Besnier, *L'Île Tibérine,* etc.; Leger, *Les Travaux,* etc.

19. Choisy, p. 161; Leger, pp. 131, 265; Jones, p. 82.

20. Cf. Vitruvius, X. 7, on " The Pump of Ctesibius."

20a. But cf. Robinson, *Excavations at Olynthus,* II, p. 39.

21. Cagnat et Chapot, vol. I, pp. 57–61; De Tissot, pp. 31–57; Durm, p. 432; F. Ferrero, pp. 120, 170–177, and chap. III; Jones, pp. 6, 13–19; Haverfield, *Town-planning,* p. 89.

22. Macdonald, *Roman Wall in Scotland;* Bruce, *Handbook;* Guest, *Origines Celticae,* vol. II, ch. 3; Ward, *Roman*

NOTES

Era, pp. 61–65; Wright, *The Celt, the Roman, and the Saxon,* p. 157; Hodgkin, *History of England,* p. 52.

23. Jones, pp. 244–256; Macdonald, pp. 263, 264, 389; Mommsen, *Provinces,* VIII, 4. pp. 132, 167; Diels, ch. 4.

24. Narducci, *Sulla Fognatura di Roma;* Burr, 29–31; Lanciani, *Ruins and Excavations,* pp. 28–31.

25. Herschel, p. 130; Lanciani, *Ruins and Excavations,* p. 15; Huxley, *Physiography,* p. 206.

26. *Brisse, Il Prosciugamento di Fucino;* Bergier, Bk. IV, XLVI, 3, 4; Drinker, pp. 10, 11; *Legacy of Rome,* p. 471; Jones, pp. 153, 154; Leger, 424, 425.

27. Horace, *Satires,* I. V. 12 *seq.*

28. Lanciani, *Ruins and Excavations,* p. 13.

29. Calza, *Ostia,* p. 156; Burr, 56, 57; Jones, p. 157; Leger, pp. 383, 456; Lanciani, *Ancient Rome,* 239, 248; *Wanderings,* p. 350.

30. *N. H.,* XXXIII, 21.

31. Alex. Del Mar, in *Engineering Magazine,* March, 1905; Bouchier, p. 87.

32. Leger, Preface, p. ii, VII.

33. Leger, pp. 739, 742; Smiles, *Life of Rennie; Catholic Encyc.,* article, " Bridge Building Brotherhood."

34. Telford, *Autobiography,* p. 258.

35. Leger, pp. 779, 780; Giovannoni, in *The Legacy of Rome,* pp. 463, 474. D. E. Smith, *Mathematics,* p. 129, in " Our Debt to Greece and Rome " Series.

36. Pliny, *Ep.,* X. 40 (cf. *Loeb Cl. Lib.*).

BIBLIOGRAPHY

ALLEN, GRANT, *Anglo-Saxon Britain*. London, 1901.

ASHBY, TH., *The Roman Campagna in Classical Times*. London, 1927.

BAILEY, C., *The Legacy of Rome*. Oxford, 1923.
(c. on Building and Engineering, pp. 429–474, by G. Giovannoni)

BELLOC, HILAIRE, *The Stane Street*. London, 1913; *The Old Road*. London, 1904; *Hills and the Sea*. New York, 1906.

BENNETT, CHARLES E., *Frontinus*, in *The Loeb Classical Library* (edited by M. B. McElwain). London and New York, 1925.

BERGIER, NICOLAS, *Histoire des Grands Chemins de l'Empire Romain*. Brussels, 1728.

BLANCHARD, A. H., and H. B. DROWNE, *Text-Book on Highway Engineering*. New York, 1913.

BLÜMNER, HUGO, *Technologie und Terminologie der Gewerbe und Künste bei Griechen und Römern*. 4 vols. Leipzig, 1875–1886. Vol. I.² 1912.

BOUCHIER, E. S., *Spain under the Roman Empire*. Oxford, 1914.

BRADLEY, HENRY, *The Goths*. New York, 1903.

BRISSE, ALEXANDRE, *Il Prosciugamento del Fucino*. Rome, 1885. *The Draining of Lake Fucino*, Eng. tr. Rome, Propaganda Press, 1876.

BRUCE, DR. J. COLLINGWOOD, *Handbook of the Roman Wall*. London, 1895.

BRUGSCH-BEY, HEINRICK, *Egypt under the Pharaohs* (translated by M. Broderick). London, 1891.

BRYCE, JAMES, *The Holy Roman Empire*. London, 1889.

BURR, W. H., *Ancient and Modern Engineering*. New York, 1903.

ENGINEERING

CAGNAT, R. ET V. CHAPOT, *Manuel d'Archéologie Romaine.* 2 vols. Paris, 1916–20.

CALZA, G., *Ostia. Historical Guide to the Monuments* (transl. by R. Weeden-Cooke). Roma, 1927.

CAMDEN, WILLIAM, *Britannia* (edited by Edmund Gibson). London, 1772.

CHOISY, AUGUSTE, *L'Art de Bâtir chez les Romains.* Paris, 1876.

COBDEN, RICHARD, *Political Writings.* New York, 1867.

CODRINGTON, T., *Roman Roads in Britain.*[3] London, 1918.

COOLIDGE, W. A. B., *The Alps in Nature and History.* New York, 1908.

COZZO, G., *Ingegneria Romana.* Rome, 1928.

DE TISSOT, PAUL, *Étude Historique et Juridique sur la Condition des Agrimensores dans l'ancienne Rome.* Nancy, 1879.

DIELS, HERMANN, *Antike Technik.*[2] Leipzig, 1920.

DRINKER, H. S., *Tunnelling.* New York, 1878.

DURM, JOSEF, *Handbuch der Architektur, die Baukunst der Etrusker und Römer.* Darmstadt, 1885. (2d. Ed., Stuttgart, 1905).

FERRERO, FELICE, *The Valley of Aosta.* New York, 1910.

FERRERO, GUGLIELMO, *The Ruins of the Ancient Civilization and the Triumph of Christianity.* New York, 1921.

FRANK, T., *Roman Buildings of the Republic.* Rome, 1924.

FRIEDLAENDER, LUDWIG, *Roman Life and Manners* (translated by L. A. Magnus and J. H. Freese). 4 vols. New York, 1913.

FROTHINGHAM, A. L., *Roman Cities in Italy,* etc. New York, 1910.

GERMAIN DE MONTAUZAN, C., *Les Aqueducs de Lyon.* Paris, 1908. *La Science et l'Art de l'Ingénieur aux premiers siècles de l'Empire Romain.* Paris, 1909.

GRANT, CAPTAIN W. A., *The Topography of Stane Street.* London, 1922.

GUEST, EDWIN, *Origines Celticae: The Four Roman Ways.* 2 vols. London, 1883.

BIBLIOGRAPHY

HADLEY, H. S., *Rome and the World Today*. New York, 1923.

HAMMERTON, J. A., *Wonders of the Past*. 4 vols. New York, 1924.

HAVERFIELD, F. J., *The Romanization of Roman Britain*. London, 1905; *Roman Britain*, in Cambridge Mediaeval History, Vol. I. New York, 1911; *Ancient Town-planning*. Oxford, 1913; *The Roman Occupation of Britain*. Oxford, 1924.

HERONIS ALEXANDRINI, *Opera*, Griech. u. Deutsch, W. Schmidt, etc. Leipzig (Teubner), 1899–1914.

HERSCHEL, CLEMENS, *Frontinus and the Water Supply of the City of Rome*. (Translation into English and explanatory chapters.) New York and London, 1913.

JONES, H. STUART, *Companion to Roman History*. Oxford, 1912.

LANCIANI, RODOLFO, *Topografia di Roma Antica, I Commentarii di Frontino intorno le Acque e gli Acquedotti*, etc. Rome, 1880; *The Ruins and Excavations of Ancient Rome*. Boston, 1897; *Ancient Rome in the Light of Recent Discoveries.*[3] Boston, 1889; *The Destruction of Ancient Rome*. New York, 1901; *Wanderings in the Roman Campagna*. New York, 1909.

LEGER, ALFRED, *Les Travaux Publics aux Temps des Romains, La Tradition Romaine jusqu'à nos Jours*. Paris, 1875.

MACDONALD, GEORGE, *The Roman Wall in Scotland*. Glasgow, 1911.

MASPERO, G., *L'Archéologie Égyptienne*. Paris, 1907.

MERCKEL, KURT, *Die Ingenieurtechnik im Alterthum*. Berlin, 1899.

MEYER, DR. H., *Die Römischen Alpenstrassen in der Schweiz* in "*Mittheilungen, Antiquarische Gesellschaft in Zurich*," Vol. 13. Zurich, 1862.

MIDDLETON, J. H., *The Remains of Ancient Rome*. 2 vols. London, 1892.

MOMMSEN, THEODORE, *History of Rome* (translated by W. P. Dickson). 5 vols. New York, 1895; *The Prov-*

inces of the Roman Empire (translated by W. P. Dickson). 2 vols. New York, 1887.

MOONEY, WILLIAM W., *Travel among the Ancient Romans*. Boston, 1920.

MORGAN, M. H., *Vitruvius, The Ten Books on Architecture*. Translation, with Illustrations and Designs. Cambridge, Massachusetts, 1914.

MUNRO, DANA CARLTON, *The Middle Ages*. New York, 1923.

NARDUCCI, PIETRO, *Sulla Fognatura della Città di Roma*. Rome, 1889.

NEUBURGER, A., *Die Technik des Altertums*.[3] Leipzig, 1921.

PARKER, J. H., *The Aqueducts of Ancient Rome*. Oxford, London, 1876.

PLATNER, S. B., *The Topography and Monuments of Ancient Rome*.[2] Boston, 1911.

PLATNER-ASHBY, *A Topographical Dictionary of Rome*. Oxford, 1929.

RAWLINSON, GEORGE, *History of Ancient Egypt*. New York, 1880.

RAWNSLEY, W. F., *Highways and By-Ways in Lincolnshire*. London, 1914.

RIVOIRA, G. T., *Architettura Romana*. Milan, 1921. (English tr., by G. McN. Rushforth, Oxford, 1925.)

ROBERTSON, D. S., *A Handbook of Greek and Roman Architecture*. Cambridge, Eng., 1929.

ROCKWELL, A. P., *Roads and Pavements in France*. London, 1896.

RONDELET, JEAN, *Traité Théorique et Pratique de l'Art de Bâtir*. 5 vols. Paris, 1842.

SANDYS, J. E., *A Companion to Latin Studies*,[2] c. VI. 10 B: "Roads and Travel," by R. C. Bosanquet. Cambridge, 1913.

SCHÖNE, HERMANN, "Die Dioptra des Heron," in *Jahrb. des Kais. D. Arch. Instituts*, XIV. 91–103 (1899); "Das Visirinstrument der Römischen Feldmesser," in *J. d. K. D. A. I.*, XVI. 127–132 (1901).

SMILES, SAMUEL, *Lives of the Engineers*. London, 1862 and 1874.

BIBLIOGRAPHY

STUKELEY, REV. WILLIAM, *Letters and Diary* in " Publications of the Surtees Society," Vols. 73, 76, 80. Durham, 1882, 1887.

TELFORD, THOMAS, *Autobiography*. London, 1838.

TERQUEM, A., *La Science Romaine*. Paris, 1885.

WADDELL, J. A. L., *Bridge Engineering*. New York, 1896.

WALTERS, R. C. SKYRING, " Greek and Roman Engineering Instruments," in *Transactions of the Newcomen Society*. Vol. II, 1921–22.

WARD, JOHN, *The Roman Era in Britain*. London, 1911.

WINDLE, B. C. A., *Life in Early Britain*. London, 1897.

WRIGHT, THOMAS, *The Celt, The Roman and the Saxon*. London, 1902.

Our Debt to Greece and Rome

AUTHORS AND TITLES

AUTHORS AND TITLES

AESCHYLUS AND SOPHOCLES. *J. T. Sheppard.*

GREEK RELIGION. *Walter Woodburn Hyde.*

SURVIVALS OF ROMAN RELIGION. *Gordon J. Laing.*

MYTHOLOGY. *Jane Ellen Harrison.*

ANCIENT BELIEFS IN THE IMMORTALITY OF THE SOUL. *Clifford H. Moore.*

STAGE ANTIQUITIES. *James Turney Allen.*

PLAUTUS AND TERENCE. *Gilbert Norwood.*

ROMAN POLITICS. *Frank Frost Abbott.*

PSYCHOLOGY, ANCIENT AND MODERN. *G. S. Brett.*

ANCIENT AND MODERN ROME. *Rodolfo Lanciani.*

WARFARE BY LAND AND SEA. *Eugene S. McCartney.*

THE GREEK FATHERS. *James Marshall Campbell.*

GREEK BIOLOGY AND MEDICINE. *Henry Osborn Taylor.*

MATHEMATICS. *David Eugene Smith.*

LOVE OF NATURE AMONG THE GREEKS AND ROMANS. *H. R. Fairclough.*

ANCIENT WRITING AND ITS INFLUENCE. *B. L. Ullman.*

GREEK ART. *Arthur Fairbanks.*

ARCHITECTURE. *Alfred M. Brooks.*

ENGINEERING. *Alexander P. Gest.*

MODERN TRAITS IN OLD GREEK LIFE. *Charles Burton Gulick.*

ROMAN PRIVATE LIFE. *Walton Brooks McDaniel.*

GREEK AND ROMAN FOLKLORE. *William Reginald Halliday.*

ANCIENT EDUCATION. *J. F. Dobson.*